INSTRUCTOR'S MANUAL

FRANCIS X. BRENNAN
Wilkes University
KYLE L. SNOW

D1244934

PHYSIOLOGICAL PSYCHOLOGY
A NEUROSCIENCE APPROACH

TIMOTHY K. SMOCK

University of Colorado at Boulder

PRENTICE HALL, Upper Saddle River, New Jersey 07458

© 1999 by PRENTICE-HALL, INC.
Upper Saddle River, New Jersey 07458

ISBN 0-13-095801-8

Printed in the United States of America

Table of Contents

CHAPTER 1: PHILOSOPHICAL ISSUES IN NEUROSCIENCE

Chapter Outline:

STUDYING THE BRAIN
- There is a literal neuroscience of everything!
- What are the most *enjoyable*, *productive*, and *elevating* behavioral pursuits, given all of our choices?
- Philosophical concerns
  -How can a mind, the subject, have enough intellectual machinery to comprehend an equally complicated mind, the object?
  -Can we fully understand the phenomenon of mind?

Practical Concerns
- Introspection: practiced in philosophy, religion, and psychology, involves the contemplation of internal thought processes
  -certainty acquired from introspection is limited
  -heuristic imagery: an image that can be eventually tested by experiment
- Received knowledge: information from, for example, sacred text
  -mathematical axioms accepted as assumptions
- Deductive Reasoning: a general statement leads to specific findings
  -consequences follow logically from the general statement
  -obvious problem is agreement on the general statements
- Scientific Method: example of inductive reasoning
  -specific observations lead to general truths
  -observation: a scientific observer perceives regularities in nature, leading to curiosity about the underlying principle
  -hypothesis: a possible underlying principle is described in the form of a statement or postulate
  -the statement must be falsifiable
  -experiment: one or more attempts to find observations that disprove the hypothesis
  -conclusion: rejection of the hypothesis if experimental observations contradict it, or cautious acceptance of the hypothesis in the form of a theory, if experiments provide consistent evidence

The Disciplines of Neuroscience
- Behaviorism: against reductionism

-reductionism: belief that behavior could be broken down into mental or brain processes
-two historical variants of reductionism:
- Physiological (biological) psychology: study of the biological basis of behavior
  -started with observed behavior, attempted to break it down into underlying mechanisms
  -Numerous subareas:
  -psychophysiology: study of the relationship between the autonomic nervous system and behavior
  -psychophysics: study of sensory stimuli and behavior
- Neurobiology: from biology and medicine
  -incorporated many scientific and medical specialities:
  -biophysics: physical chemistry as applied to ion channels and receptors
  -neuroanatomy: anatomy of the brain
  -neurochemistry: chemistry of the brain
  -neurophysiology: function of the brain
  -neuropharmacology: effect of drugs on the brain
- Physiological psychology and neurobiology were two separate disciplines until neuroscience emerged as an amalgam of the two in the 1970s.

THE MIND/BODY PROBLEM
- Humans have always searched for the location of the soul
  -Is the soul physical or spiritual?
  -Which organ of the body contains it?
  -Historically, the brain has not been seen as important as the liver, blood, or heart
  -Quest for the soul in philosophy is the mind/body problem

Hippocrates and Aristotle
- Hippocrates: in Western history, first to record an opinion on the connection between mental events and the brain
  -observed individuals with brain injuries and inferred that mental function was a property of brain function
  -monism: mind and body are identical
- Aristotle: Dualism: mind and body are separate
  -postulated a nonphysical entity that worked jointly with the brain

Descartes
- Most Western thinking since Artistotle, and all Christianity, is inherently dualistic

-he favored a form of dualism where interaction occurred through the pineal gland, called interactionist dualism
-absolute dualism proposes there is no communication at all between the physical and spiritual realms

Berkeley and La Mettrie

- Monistic challenges to Descartes
    -Berkeley: spiritual monism, all reality is spiritual
    -La Mettrie: material monism, all reality is material

Do you have to choose?

- Sherrington: monism as sterile and deprived life of meaning
    -materialistic monism inconsistent with free will
    -emergent property dualism: the mind may be a function of the physical brain, but the whole is greater then the sum of its parts
    -Heisenberg uncertainty principle: from physics, holds that the behavior of some subatomic particles is unknowable, avenue for free will to overcome cause and effect
    -Chaos: hope for indeterminancy in mental processes and free will

TELEOLOGY VS. DEONTOLOGY

- Natural philosophy: study of nature
    -deontology: nature, as the object of creation, is marvelously complex
    -any purpose in mind of God in designing nature was too complex for our intellects
    -teleology: the mind of God is rational, therefore creation must be rational
    -our minds therefore could understand the purpose and order behind creation

Does life have a purpose?

- According to teleologists, each animal and plant has a divine purpose
    -often their purpose was perceived to be for our use
    -life had a divine purpose because of God's creation, but also a continuing purpose in which all parts work together

Darwin's Theory

- Rejected the notion of divine creation, but still teleological
    -no useless structures or behaviors could survive
    -anything that emerged from evolution must have utiltiy
    -there may be larger chunks of useless information in DNA

Teleological Reasoning

- Applied throughout the text
    - -e.g., what is the purpose of surround inhibition?
    - -some answers are plausible, some debatable

THE WHOLE AND THE PARTS
- Brain and spinal cord are different from other organs in the body
    - -connected to other organs via the peripheral nervous system
    - -brain and spinal cord are the central nervous system

Neurohumors
- Many medieval scholars thought the cardiovascular system was the seat of the soul
    - -differences in mood were seen as reflecting differences in four body humors: bile, blood, phlegm, etc.
    - -currently, global agents are called humoral agents or neurohumors
    - -humoral agents are chemicals such as hormones and transmitters
    - -da Vinci, during the Renaissance, believed that the ventricular system and associated fluid were critical for mind

The Patients, and Patience, of Paul Broca
- The brain as the producer of behavior instead of the circulation gained support after the Middle Ages and people survived brain injuries
    - -Gall examined patients with abnormalities and dissected their brains after death
    - -developed the theory of phrenology, the idea that specific traits were located in specific brain areas, and caused changes in the skull that could be read
    - -although phrenology was wrong, it led to the field of diagnostic neurology
    - -Broca was a follower of Gall interested in aphasias, failures in communication
    - -Broca's and Wernicke's areas describes as part of a left hemispheric circuit

The Law of Equipotentiality
- Diagnostic neurology contradicted medieval notions that behaviors were evenly distributed throughout the body
    - -evidence for regional specialization
    - -however, other evidence did support widely distributed functions
    - -Lashley searched for the engram, the physical basis of memory

-large brain lesions did not disrupt maze learning
-Lashley called his discovery the "law of equipotentiality"
-aggregate field theory: whole brain or large sections involved in a behavior
-cellular connectionism: discrete brain regions involved

Parallel versus. Serial Processing

- Computer scientists and cognitive psychologists have developed numerous ideas about mental processes independently of biological findings
  -cognitive neuroscience as the coalescence of neuroscience and cognitive psychology
  -serial processing: analog computers; cellular connectionism
  -parallel processing: supercomputers;   aggregate field theory

Lecture Topics:

1. Hippocrates came to a monistic conclusion regarding the mind/body problem after observing patients with brain injuries. Given that many students will know someone who has suffered a traumatic head injury, discuss the mind/body problem and how a dualist might explain personality changes following brain injury.

2. The discussion in Box 1-2 about solipsism and cultural relativism can lead to several interesting areas of discussion. Is it true that the only reality is cultural? Have American universities been "Western biased" in their required curricula? Was Shakespeare objectively great, or only great given our cultural background?

3. The discussion of phrenology as a pseudoscience can lead logically to a discussion of some "fringe" areas of science and medicine. What is the evidence that therapeutic touch and energy fields are legitimate phenomena? Also, many professional athletes now wear magnets on various parts of their bodies to reduce pain. What are the empirical data regarding these manipulations?

Overhead Transparencies:

1. The four steps of the scientific method from p. 4.

2. Table 1-1: The Disciplines of Neuroscience.

3. Figure 1-6: The Central and Peripheral Nervous Systems.

4. Figure 1-8: The Lobes of the Brain.

Classroom Demonstrations/Student Activities:

1. Have the students generate a list of five a priori general statements that they are certain are true. Make a list on the board of the statements that the students generate. Are there several that appear numerous times? Does anyone disagree with any of the statements?

Handouts:

1. Table 1-1: The Disciplines of Neuroscience.

Video List:

Consciousness. From the series "The Human Quest." Excellent discussion of mind-brain issues from a perspective of contemporary neuroscience.

CHAPTER 2: THE CELLULAR BASIS OF BEHAVIOR

Chapter Outline:

NEURON DOCTRINE VERSUS. RETICULAR THEORY
- Cell theory was the idea that the unit of life was the nucleus, surrounded by a fluid perikaryon, and separated from other cells by the cell membrane
    - biologists sought to apply cell theory to the brain
    - reticular theory was the notion that the brain was not composed of cells, but was a dense, continuous network
    - the neuron doctrine was the belief that the brain was composed of individual cells called neurons

Golgi's Stain
- Golgi was a devoted proponent of reticular theory
    - he discovered a number of structures
    - also discovered the Golgi stain, or the silver impregnation technique, a method for visualizing individual cells
    - Golgi's stain used by Santiago Ramon y Cajal
    - Ramon y Cajal became a proponent of the neuron doctrine
    - Cajal believed that neurons were the units of integration

Parts of the Neuron
- Neurons vary in structure from one part of the brain to another
    - each had a perikaryon, which he called the soma
    - Cajal called the nerve fibers emerging from the soma neurites
    - cells with one neurite are monopolar cells
    - cells with two neurites are bipolar cells
    - cells with several neurites are multipolar cells
    - neurites branched near the soma are dendrites
    - the neurite that traveled far away from the soma was the axon
    - enlargements at the end of the axon are the boutons
    - neurons contained structures in common with all cells, such as chromosomes, ribosomes, endoplasmic reticulum, etc.

"The Law of Dynamic Polarization"
- Ramon y Cajal surmised function from structure
    - dendrites specialized to receive information
    - axons specialized to create output
    - called this the "law of dynamic polarization"
    - states that information flows from the dendrite to soma to axon, then to dendrite of another cell

-many exceptions to the "law"
-e.g., axosomatic, axoaxonic, and axosynaptic connections exist
-revised law might be that information always flows from presynaptic to postsynaptic side
-sensory neurons bring information into the CNS
-motor neurons transmit information to muscles
-interneurons, the greatest number, lie between sensory and motor neurons

THE PLASMA MEMBRANE

- A site of many important brain events
  -intracellular environment is inside of cells
  -extracellular environment is outside of cells

Hydrophilicity and Hydrophobicity

- Two thirds of the body is made up of water
  -fat molecules sometimes acquire a phosphorous group at one end, thus are called phospholipids
  -charged structures that can interact with water are called hydrophilic (water-loving)
  -uncharged structures that are unable to interact with water are hydrophobic (water fearing)
  -some molecules are amphipathic, meaning they have a hydrophobic and hydrophilic region
  -phospholipids, the major constituent of cell membranes, form a bilayer of hydrophobic insides and hydrophilic outsides

A "Fluid Mosaic"

- The hydrophobic interior of the bilayer would be a barrier to any charged particle getting into the cell
  -proteins exist in the membrane
  -they form hydrophilic channels and pumps
  -proteins are floating in the membrane, thus the membrane is often called a fluid mosaic

GENETICS IN A NUTSHELL

- Simple organic materials can join together chemically into polymers
  -one polymer, containing the sugar ribose phosphate and either adenine, guanine, cytosine, or uracil is ribonucleic acid, or RNA
  -RNA has the ability to self-replicate

-RNA directs the synthesis of protein, which is composed of amino acids

-deoxyribonucleic acid, or DNA, is a polymer of deoxyribose and the RNA bases, with thymine replacing uracil

A Four Letter Code

- The four DNA bases are assembled into the DNA polymer in a sequence specific to one's hereditary information

  -two DNA strands form a double helix, with base pairs binding to complementary base pairs

  -regions of DNA are promoters, which are sites for nucleic acid synthesis and are associated with particular genes, the units of heredity

  -RNA polymerase interacts with with the DNA and makes an RNA copy of the gene, called transcription

  -messenger RNA (mRNA) is produced by transcription

  -mRNA interacts with ribosomes to form protein

A Twenty-Letter Alphabet

- At the ribosomes, the mRNA is read by transfer RNA (tRNA)

  -each tRNA molecule carries with it one of 20 amino acids

  -a three base sequence representing an amino acid is a codon

  -the complete list of codons for the 20 amino acids is the genetic code

  -translation is the formation of proteins from mRNA

  -some amino acids function as transmitter molecules

SOME PROTEINS IMPORTANT TO CELL FUNCTION

Structural Proteins

- Ribosomes bound to the endoplasmic reticulum produce proteins that are bound to the plasma membrane, and others that are released from the cell

  -free ribosomes produce enzymes and structural proteins

  -actin and tubulin form structures that help determine cell shape

Enzymes

- Many chemical reactions are accelerated by catalysts that cause them to create products from substrates

  -If a catalyst is a protein, it is called an enzyme

  -nonproteins that work with enzymes are coenzymes

Receptors and Channels

- Amphipathic proteins become embedded in the membrane as they are synthesized

  -some form channels and pumps

-others form binding sites for transmitter molecules
-binding sites recognizing transmitter is called stereochemical attraction
-a ligand is a small molecule that binds to a protein
-the degree of attraction between a ligand and a receptor is affinity
-many receptors contain sugars and are called glycoproteins
-glycoproteins perform a variety of functions including complex channels and receptors

THE ACTIVE NEURON

- Proteins provide the avenue for the inside of the cell to exchange molecules with the outside
    -for complex organisms, the outside is cerebrospinal fluid (CSF)
    -the energy provided by food is made available via a three step process
    -glycolysis is the breakdown of glucose
    -glycolysis produces a net gain of two molecules of ATP
    -pyruvate, the end product of glycolysis, enters the Krebs cycle (aerobic metabolism)
    -the Krebs cycle produces NADH
    -NADH transports protons in the mitochondria

Axoplasmic Transport

- Newly synthesized protein must be transported to distant locations in the neurites, called axoplasmic transport
    -orthograde or anterograde transport is away from the soma
    -retrograde transport is towards the soma
    -axoplasmic transport can be either slow or fast
    -structural proteins like microtubules, neurofilaments, and actin filaments make up a network that produces axoplasmic transport

Exocytosis and Endocytosis

- Vesicles in orthograde transport become coated with clathrin as they approach the plasma membrane
    -exocytosis is the fusion of the vesicle with the plasma membrane
    -any vesicular contents are dumped into the extracellular fluid
    -the opposite of exocytosis is endocytosis, where a piece of the membrane pinches back to form a new vesicle

The Neuron in Development

- Early in embryonic development, neurons begin to send out neuritic processes
  - during axon growth, exocytosis exceeds endocytsis
  - axons connect with a target cell and form synapses
  - endo and exosytosis are precisely balanced in a mature synapse
  - the chemoaffinity hypothesis is one explanation of how neurites find their way during development
  - chemical signals, called trophic factors, may be exchanged between potential synaptic partners
  - nerve growth factor is one trophic factor
  - the tip of a growing axon is called a growth cone
  - presynaptic and postsynaptic densities of protein appear in mature synapses
  - postsynaptic receptors can up-regulate and down-regulate based upon the amount of trophic factor they are receiving
  - the chemoaffinity hypothesis was tested by Roger Sperry in a series of experiments
  - rotating newt eyes caused the nerves to attach to their original targets, even though they were now in the wrong locations
  - CNS damage is permanent, and appears to result from the glial cells oligodendrocytes
  - PNS glial cells are Schwann cells

Lecture Topics:

1.   Scientists now believe that protocells and therefore possibly life, began spontaneously because of the intrinsic characteristics of the molecules involved. Ask the students if they agree with this, and what implications, if any, does this finding have for religous beliefs?

2.   Our increased understanding of the genome can lead to a number of discussion topics. For example, can we advance to the point where parents can pick out in advance the physical and mental characteristics of their future baby? If we get to this point, should we do this?

3.   The students should be familiar with the cloning of various animals. If and when we get to the point of cloning humans, what

are the pluses and minuses of the procedure? Should we do this if we can? Would a clone really be the same person?

Overhead Transparencies:

1. Figure 2-5: Types of Neurons.

2. Figure 2-6: The Anatomy of the Neuron.

3. Figure 2-11: The Phospholipid Bilayer.

4. Figure 2-20(b): The Plasma Membrane.

5. Figure 2-33: Chemoaffinity on the CNS.

Classroom Demonstrations/Student Activities:

1. Break the students down into small groups and have them discuss these questions: Would they want to know the gender of their baby before it was born? Would they want to know if their baby had any genetic diseases before it was born? Would they choose to terminate a pregnancy based solely on genetic information learned? These controversial questions should produce a lively discussion about the pros and cons of genetic testing, and our knowledge of the genome in general.

Handouts:

1. Figure 2-15: Transcription.

Video List:

Cell Evolution. Describes the synthesis of organic molecules before life began, and how self-replication may have begun.

CHAPTER 3: COMMUNICATION AMONG NEURONS: THE MEMBRANE POTENTIAL

Chapter Outline:

THE BASICS OF CHEMISTRY
- All matter is formed of atoms, and each atom belongs to a family of particles called   elements
    - elements differ in their structure; the positively charged nucleus and the negatively charged electrons
    - most atoms have a vacancy in one or more of their electron orbitals
    - this causes different atoms to bond together in aggregates called molecules
    - much life exists in the ocean, which is a vast reservoir of water
    - the water molecule is composed of two hydrogen atoms and one oxygen atom
    - Atoms and molecules that have either lost or gained a charge are called ions
    - positively charged ions are called cations
    - negatively charged ions are called anions
    - the amount of hydrogen ion in a given reservoir of water is described by the pH scale
    - salt (NaCl) exists in water as free ion

Opposite Charges Attract
- Opposite charges attract and like charges repel
    - a negatively charged surface attracts positive ions and is called a cathode
    - a positively charged surface attracts negative ions and is called an anode

Quantity and Concentration
- Number of particles is described in moles
    - actual amounts not as important as concentrations
    - one mole per liter is a molar solution
    - the prefix milli- means a thousandth of

A SEMIPERMEABLE MEMBRANE
- Each cell is surrounded by a phospholipid bilayer
    - the membrane has a hydrophobic region that prevents water or ions from crossing

-charged particles can only pass through a pore or channel in the membrane

-the chemical compostion of the intracellular and extracellular environments is different

sea water and blood are very similar in their chemical composition

-the intracellular environment is rich in potassium

-the extracellular environment is rich in sodium

-many anionic proteins and amino acids exist inside the cell and balance out the charge

Entropy and Enthalpy

- The membranous balls of seawater probably formed around RNA, which aided in the replication of the protocell

  -Proteins spanned the membrane and allowed ions to enter and leave the cell

  -a collection of these proteins is a polymer

  -entropy is the measure of disorder in a system

  -entropy makes any system less organized

  -entropy causes diffusion, which is the movement of ions from areas of high to areas of low concentration

  -entropy will push potassium out of the cell

  -enthalpy is the principle of opposites attracting

  -potassium will tend to be pulled into the cell by entropy

  -equilibrium is the point where entropy and enthalpy balance each other out for a given ion species

An "Equilibrium Potential" for Potassium

- The Nernst equation quantifies the equilibrium potential for a given ion species

MEASURING THE MEMBRANE POTENTIAL

- The Nernst equation can be used to calculate the amount of negative charge inside the cell caused by the exit of potassium, or to calculate the concentration gradient from the potential

Polarity and Ground

- An electrode can be inserted into the intracellular environment to measure the charge

  -ground is the external charge referent used to make comparisons meaningful

  -the choice of the outside concentration of potassium as the numerator is arbitrary

Depolarization and Hyperpolarization

- Data from the cell membrane are displayed as traces on an oscilloscope screen
    - any movement that decreases the difference in charge at rest is a depolarization
    - any movement that increases the difference in charge at rest is a hyperpolarization

THREE FORCES AND THREE GATES

- The measured membrane potential is close to the equilibrium potential for potassium, but not identical
    - other forces in addition to potassium are contributing to the membrane potential

Nernst Values for Sodium and Chloride

- Sodium and chloride are the other factors contibuting to the membrane potential
    - the equilibrium potential for sodium is +56 mV
    - the equilibrium potential for chloride is -66 mV
    - the three forces (E_K, E_{Na}, and E_{Cl}) combine to produce the membrane potential

Permeability Ratios

- The actual resting potential is far from the value for sodium because the sodium channel has less of a tendency to let sodium in than the other channels
    - sodium has a smaller permeability ratio
    - how can a channel be selective?
    - sodium does contribute the least to the membrane potential

The Goldman Equation

- The Goldman Equation solves for the membrane potential (E_m), using the concentration gradients for all three ions, plus the permeability ratios
    - the value of E_m obtained from the Goldman equation is -67 mV, 3 mV less negative than the actual -70 mV

The Sodium/Potassium pump

- Axon preparations gradually approached the value of -67 mV after removed from the organism
    - there must be an energy-consuming process that causes the 3 mV hyperpolarizing influence
    - this process is an enzyme, the sodium/potassium pump
    - the pump moves out three sodium ions for every two potassium ions moved into the cell
    - the pump is the predominant energy-consuming process in the brain

THE "EQUIVALENT CIRCUIT"

- The equilibrium potentials are literally batteries
   - the equivalent circuit is a model of the membrane potential concentrating on batteries (the forces) and conductors (gates)

Batteries and Conductors

- Ohm's law is a description of electrical processes:
   - $V = IR$
   - V is potential in volts
   - I is current in amps
   - R is resistance in ohms
   - the reciprocal of resistance is conductance, which is measured in mhos
   - when conductance is high, curent flows readily; the equilibrium potentials are the batteries
   - the channels are the conductances

Constancy of the Batteries

- The Na/K pump will keep the gradients exactly the same in healthy organism
   - The batteries never change

Variability of the Conductances

- The values of the conductances change in response to voltage signals
   - each ion "wants" the membrane potential to equal its own equilibrium potential
   - this degree to which this"desire" can be accomplished depends on the relative conductance

Lecture Topics:

1.   The intracellular environment leads to some interesting topics about the origin of life. Sodium and chloride exist outside the cell, in concentrations similar to sea water. This would lead to the conclusion that life evolved in the ocean, except for the potassium-rich intracellular environment. Did life evolve in a potassium-rich fresh water enviroment, and then get washed out to sea? Is there any way we could ever find out?

2.   A strict monist would argue that all mental activity is nothing but brain activity. Identify students that are strict monists, and ask them if the assertion that their most powerful thoughts, dreams,

and emotions are really nothing more than ions crossing membranes is disturbing.

3. The fact that the resting membrane potentials is the same in humans and giant squids brings up an interesting topic about the nature of our intellect. Since the fundamental processes are the same in both a "primitive" squid and an "advanced" human, is our intelligence simply due to quantitative rather than qualitative differences from other species?

Overhead Transparencies:

1. Figure 3-2: Anode and Cathode.

2. Figure 3-6: Entropy and Electrostatic Forces in Balance.

3. Figure 3-9: The Sodium/Potassium Pump.

4. Figure 3-10: The Equivalent Circuit.

5. Table 3-1: Common Scientific Units.

Handouts:

1. Table 3-1: Common Scientific Units.

Video List:

Neurophysiology. University of Illinois. Neuromuscular transmission, activity of sodium-potassium ions during the spike and resting potential, and graphs of neural activity are displayed.

CHAPTER 4: COMMUNICATION AMONG NEURONS:
THE ACTION POTENTIAL

Chapter Outline:

THE ELECTRICALLY EXCITABLE DOMAIN
- Events in the soma and dendrites are electrical changes initiated by a chemical signal and changes in the axon and bouton are electrical changes initiated by an electrical signal.
    - small hyperpolarizations occur to small injections of negative current
    - larger depolarizations produce a region of instability in current/voltage relationship, producing a waveform called the action potential

An All-or-None Event
- Action potentials are abrupt depolarizations that are the basis for neural signaling in the electrically excitable domain
    - the first phase is a rapid depolarizationthat takes the membrane potential past zero, approaching the sodium equilibrium potential
    - next is a hyperpolarizing phase where the membrane potential passes zero and becomes close to the potassium equilibrium potential
    - a third phase returns the membrane potential to the resting value
    - an action potential is all-or-none, meaning that they are all the same

Threshold and Refractoriness
- The value of a stimulus just sufficient to produce an action potential is called the threshold
    - superthreshold stimuli presented in rapid succession do not all produce action potentials, a state of inexcitability called refractoriness

The Real Basis of the Action Potential
- The batteries don't change, so the membrane potential must be fluctuating because the relative contributions of the batteries are changing
    - the real basis of the action potential is found in the conductance values of the three ion species
    - we can "clamp" the membrane at a particular value, using the voltage clamp procedure, to study the conductances

THE ACTION POTENTIAL EXPLAINED

- We can hold voltage constant with the voltage clamp, measure current, and then calculate conductance, using Ohm's law

Two Currents Drive the Action Potential

- Shortly after a cell is clamped, a inward positive current begins. This current peaks in approximately one half of a millisecond, and only lasts about 3 milliseconds.

  -a millisecond after the clamp is turned on, an outward positive current begins

  -this second current never stops as long as the clamp is maintained

The Effects of Toxins on Current

- Removal of sodium eliminates the depolarizing current

  -tetrodotoxin (TTX) blocks the sodium channel and also eliminates the inward depolarizing current

  -removal of chloride has no effect on the outward current

  -removal of intracellular potassium elimated the outward current

  -tetraethylammonium (TEA) blocks the potassium channel and also blocks the outward current

How Conductances Create the Waveform

- An electrical signal (threshold) causes the sodium conductance to increase to a substantially higher value.

  -the sodium conductance is voltage dependent

  -the sodium conductance is also time dependent because it turns itself off

  -the potassium conductance is also voltage dependent and begins to increases just as the sodium conductance is declining

FUNCTIONS OF THE SODIUM CHANNEL

- The channel is composed of four monomers, each of which spans the membrane six times

  -certain parts of the amino acid chain produce the properties of ion selectivity, and voltage and time dependence

The Sodium Channel as a Selectivity Filter

- Ion selectivity can't be based on size

  -selectivity can't be based on charge either

The Sodium Channel as a Voltage Sensor

- A few positively charged amino acids are free to block the channel

-depolarization causes this amino acid section to reorient and unblock the channel

The Sodium Channel as a Time Sensor
- The voltage sensitive gate is connected to a molecular timer
    -the timer allows the gate to stay open for only a millisecond

The Sodium Channel as an Inactivation Mechanism
- There is another gate on the cytoplasmic side of the membrane that can also block the channel
    -this inactivation gate produces the refractory period by making the gate closed regardless of the state of the other gate and timer

FUNCTIONS OF THE POTASSIUM CHANNEL
- The properties of the potassium channel are in functional harmony with the sodium channel

The Potassium Channel as a Selectivity Filter
- The potassium channel is larger than the sodium channel
    -therefore sodium cannot be excluded based on size

The Potassium Channel as a Voltage Sensor
- Like sodium channel, the sensor causes the gate to open when the membrane is depolarized
    -there is no inactivation mechanism for the potassium channel
    -the channel will remain open until the membrane potential hyperpolarizes below the sensor's threshold

The Potassium Channel as a Delay Mechanism
- There is a timing mechanism in the potassium channel
    -the timer delays the opening of the gate for a millisecond or so after depolarization
    -this allows the sodium conductance to depolarize the cell
    -the two channels exquisitely complement the function of each other

HETEROGENEITY AND HOMOLOGY
- Most channel types come in more than one version, called heterogeneity
    -heterogeneity allows some proteins to do the same thing, even though they come from different genes
    -potassium but not sodium channels are heterogeneous
    -heterogeneity also exists with enzymes, receptors, and hormones
    -despite heterogeneity, there is substantial similarity among unrelated proteins, called homology

-a useful sequence of amino acids was retained by evolution and applied to different purposes
-the simple systems approach, or the study of simple nervous systems, can tell us alot about ourselves because of homology

THE "EQUIVALENT CIRCUIT" REVISITED
- The membrane is represented as a closed circuit which can conduct an electrical current
  -the entire equivalent circuit moves down the axon
  -there is a leading wave of depolarization and a trailing wave of depolarization

The Teleology of Refractoriness and Myelin
- Action potentials don't reverse back up the axon because of sodium channel inactivation
  -conduction in this direction is called orthodromic flow
  -the opposite, antidromic flow, is observed only experimentally
  -larger diameter axons conduct faster than smaller diameter axons
  -myelinated cells transmit faster because the equivalent circuit will be larger

Saltatory Conduction
- The presence of myelin increases the size of the equivalent circuit so that it occupies three nodes of Ranvier and two myelinated regions
  -saltatory conduction is the transmission of the action potential down a myelinated axon

Extracellular Records of Neural Activity
- Most of our information about the neuron comes from extracellular electrodes
  -the extracellular manifestation of the action potential will be a triphasic waveform
  -extracellular recording from an individual cell is called a single unit recording
  -a recording where several cells can be distinguished is a multiunit recording
  -field potential recording is recording of a number of cells where individual cells can't be differentiated
  -electroencephalography (EEG) is a field potential recording where the electrodes are outside the skull

SPECIAL CHANNELS FOR CALCIUM

- The electrically excitable domain must also transmit information across the synapse
    - this requires a third class of channels, for calcium

Presynaptic Calcium Channels

- The action potential becomes longer in shape when it enters the bouton
    - there are voltage-dependent calcium channels that exist only at the bouton
    - calcium enters the cell and depolarizes the bouton

Vesicle Fusion and Exocytosis

- Within the bouton are vesicles that contain the transmitter molecules
    - calcium and the enzyme calmodulin faciltate the fusion of the vesicle to the plasma membrane
    - the place in the membrane where this occurs is the active zone
    - exocytosis cause the release of transmitter into the synapse
    - each act of exocytosis must be balanced by an act of endocytosis for the cell to remain the same size

Lecture Topics:

1. The action potential is essentially a binary message, either firing or not firing. Is the brain literally a computer, with all of its billions of circuits functioning in binary capacity?

2. Discuss the role of refractoriness in the development of action potentials. What might the function of these times of inexcitability be?

3. Since myelinated cells transmit information faster, why isn't every cell in the brain myelinated? Have the students discuss the teleology of myelin and what pathways they would choose to be the fastest or slowest.

Overhead Transparencies:

1. Figure 4-1: Current/Voltage Relations.

2. Figure 4-2: Superimposed Action Potentials.

3. Figure 4-5: Conductances Create the Action Potential.

4. Figure 4-10: The Active Equivalent Circuit.

5. Figure 4-11: Saltatory Conduction.

Handouts:

1. Box 4-1: The Squid Giant Axon and the Voltage Clamp.

Video List:

The Nervous Impulse. Indiana University. Demonstrations of classical research studies ranging from simple frog-muscle preparations to research with the single squid-axon preparation.

The Nervous System: Nerves at Work. Indiana University. Explains the transmission of nerve impulses and discusses the chemical and electrical activities involved.

CHAPTER 5: COMMUNICATION AMONG NEURONS:
THE SYNAPTIC POTENTIAL

Chapter Outline:

THE CHEMICALLY EXCITABLE DOMAIN
- Everything that happens in the chemically excitable domain is the same as the electrically excitable domain, except for the signal that opens the gates.
    - the chemically excitable domain experiences postsynaptic potentials, which are incremental
    - the first piece of excitable membrane is the axon hillock
    - synaptic potentials are classified according to their effect on the axon hillock
    - synaptic potentials conducive to action potential

Excitatory Postsynaptic Potentials
- EPSPs may occur in one of three ways
    - the first is a postsynaptic increase in sodium conductance
    - the second is an increase in calcium conductance
    - a decrease in potassium conductance is the third mechanism

Inhibitory Postsynaptic Potentials
- Two IPSP mechanisms are widely used by the brain
    - potassium efflux is one of the mechanisms
    - this can be demonstrated by using a reversal potential
    - a bridge circuit can be used to acquire voltage measurments at the same time
- increased chloride conductance is another IPSP mechanism
    - although increases in chloride conductance would be slightly depolarizing, it tends to produce a chloride shunt, or short-circuit for other circuits in the area

SUMMATION AND INTEGRATION
- Integration is the dendrite reducing hundreds of synaptic contacts into action potentials.
    - spatial summation is the adding together of EPSPs or IPSPs over space
    - temporal summation is the adding together of EPSPs and IPSPs over time
    - summation also works in the opposite direction, in that a strong IPSP and a strong EPSP will cancel each other out
    - IPSPs often occur in the absence of excitation

-inhibition is probably a more important brain process than excitation

SPECIAL CHANNELS FOR CALCIUM
- There are special channels for calcium postsynaptically as well as presynaptically.

Postsynaptic Calcium Channels
>   -it is unclear how common postsynaptic calcium channels are
>   -recordings from distal dendrites show calcium spikes as would be seen in the bouton

THE QUANTAL NATURE OF SYNAPTIC TRANSMISSION
- Mechanisms of communication between cells resembles a language

Theories of Quantal Transmission
- Units of synaptic transmission are called quanta
>   -quanta can be studied best when presynaptic action potential activity is eliminated
>   -bits of synaptic transmission occur in the absence of action potentials, and are all the same size
>   -these spontaneous events are assumed to be equal to one quantum
>   -synaptic transmission is quantal because of variability in the number of vesicles that undergo exocytosis

RECEPTOR THEORY
- There is a region of postsynaptic density at regions of synaptic contact
>   -postsynaptic densities indicate a high level of protein
>   -most of the postsynaptic proteins are receptors
>   -a ligand is any substance that binds to the receptors
>   -receptor proteins are similar to the voltage-gated channel proteins, made up of monomeric subunits that constitute a pore specific for an individual ion species
>   -receptor proteins also display heterogeneity and homology
>   -receptors, however, have a binding site for the ligand and a gate that opens or closes when the binding site is occupied
>   -the nicotinic acetylcholine receptor is representative of a class of receptors for gamma-aminobutyric acid and glycine
>   -in some cases the receptor protein and the ion channel are different polymers that communicate through intracellular enzymes

-the transmitter molecule never passes through the postsynaptic membrane

<u>Two Types of Ligands</u>

- Transmitters actually have a continuum of efficacy

-affinity is the concept that describes how fast a ligand binds to a receptor

-potency describes how biologically effective a ligand is once it is bound to a receptor

-agonists are ligands that bind to a receptor and activate it biologically

-antagonists are ligands that bind to a receptor but have no potency

- antagonists generally have high affinity, so the receptor is literally blocked from the agonist

-the body may produce several agonists for a given receptor, but never produces an antagonist

-endogenous refers to substances that the body manufactures

-exogenous refers to foreign substances

-antagonists are always exogenous, some agonists are exogenous as well

-receptors are generally named for the antagonists that bind to them

-the other major acetylcholine receptor subtype is the muscarinic receptor, and is named for muscarine, a weak agonist

-allosteric modifiers bind to a receptor, but in a different location than agonists and antagonists

ACETYLCHOLINE

<u>Synthesis and Breakdown</u>

- Acetylcholine was the first transmitter described and is still the best understood

- acetylcholine is synthesized in the bouton from the fusion of acetate and choline, via the enzyme cholineacetyltransferase

-three mechanisms exist to terminate synaptic potentials

-the first is desensitization, meaning receptors become less responsive to the presence of the agonist

-the second mechanism is simple diffusion away from the synaptic cleft, used by only a few peptide transmitters

-the third mechanism is probably the most significant physiologically, and it involves enzymes in the extracellular matrix breaking down the transmitter molecule

-acetylcholinesterase (AChE) is the enzyme that breaks down acetylcholine
-physostigmine is a naturally occurring drug that blocks AChE
-insecticides are manmade AChE blockers that are more potent
-a cell's choice of transmitter is its phenotype

The Neuromuscular Junction

* The connection between a motor neuron and a skeletal muscle is the neuromuscular junction, and is cholinergic
    -the postsynaptic side of the neuromuscular junction is called an end plate, and has end plate potentials
    -excitation and inhibition are properties of the receptor, not the transmitter molecule

GAMMA-AMINOBUTYRIC ACID (GABA)

* Almost everywhere it is encountered, GABA produces inhibition.
    -some GABA receptors activate a potassium conductance, while others produce a chloride conductance
    -given the importance of inhibition, GABA may be the most commonly employed transmitter

Synthesis and Breakdown

* GABA, as its name implies, is an amino acid
    -GABA is made from glutamic acid, one of the 20 amino acids that can make protein
    -the enzyme glutamic acid decarboxylase (GAD) removes a carboxyl group from to produce GABA
    -a second enzyme, GABA transaminase, recycles GABA into glutamate for re-uptake and resynthesis

Allosteric Sites

* The GABA receptor type that posesses a chloride channel is homologous with other transmitter-activated ion channels
    -there are at least two allosteric binding sites on that receptor
    -one is the site of action of the benzodiazepines, the other the site of action of barbiturates
    -these compounds do not open the chloride channel, but increase the affinity of the GABA binding site for GABA

Importance in Brain

* The majority of synapses in the brain are inhibitory, therefore GABAergic
    -many synapses use the mechanism of presynaptic inhibition, where GABA blocks the bouton from the incoming action potential

-GABA antagonists produce excitation, or even seizures in a behaving animal
-epilepsy is often treated with GABA agonists

GLUTAMATE, ASPARTATE, AND GLYCINE
- Glutamate, very chemically similar to GABA, mediates most excitation in the brain
    -it is unclear whether glutamate or aspartate (or both) is the excitatory transmitter, since both are present in all cells as amino acid precursors to protein
    -glycine is an important amio acid for inhibtion, especially in the spinal cord, where it takes the place of GABA

CATECHOLAMINES, INDOLAMINE, AND HISTAMINE
- A family of transmitters, the catecholamines are synthesized from the amino acid precursor tyrosine
    -tyrosine hydroxylase (TOH) is the enzyme that converts tyrosine into an amino acid not used in making protein
    -aromatic amino acid decarboxylase makes dopamine from L-dopa
    -some cells contain the enzyme dopamine beta-hydroxylase, which converts dopamine into norepinephrine
    -logically, all noradrenergic cells also contain dopamine
    -finally, some cells also contain the enzyme phenylethanalomine N-methyltransferase (PNMT), which converts norepinephrine into epinephrine
    -epinephrine functions primarily in the peripheral nervous system
    -TOH is the rate-limiting enzyme in the chain, and allosteric sites on TOH bind to dopamine and norepinephrine, producing negative feedback
    -serotonin is an indolamine transmitter synthesized from tryptophan
    -histamine is a transmitter synthesized from histidine
    -these transmitters are collectively called biogenic amines

PEPTIDE SYNTHESIS
- A long chain of amino acids is a protein, a short chain is a peptide
Special Properties
- With some exceptions, peptides must be synthesized in the soma and sent down the axon via orthograde axoplasmic transport

-peptides are first synthesized in a large protein precursor, then cleaved into smaller active peptides

-peptides either diffuse away from the synapse, or are broken down by enzymes in a process called proteolysis

- since peptide transmitters are "metabolically expensive," they tend to act at low concentrations for a long period of time

Simple Systems
- An understanding of peptidergic transmission was first achieved using simple systems

    -Substance P was the first first peptide transmitter described

    -Substance P certainly has an important role in spinal cord and brain, but its function is much better understood in the peripheral nervous system

Endorphins
- A family of peptides exists, the endorphins, that have a receptor antagonist to them

    -naloxone is the antagonist, and has been used to identify methionine enkephalin as a transmitter in parts of the brain

Vasopressin and Oxytocin
- Vasopressin and oxytocin are hormones that also appear to act as transmitters

    -peptides also display homology and heterogeneity

    -oxytocin and vasopressin are structurally similar, and are thus homologous

    -current estimates are that as many as 300 peptides funciton as probable transmitters in human brain

THE CONCEPT OF NEUROMODULATION
- The large number of neurotransmitters presents the possibility of great complexity in chemical signaling

    -peptides are often cotransmitters, released with other transmitters

    -the term neuromodulator has been proposed for substances that act only by influencing the action of another transmitter

    -that definition lacks precision, however, so a more precise use of neuromodulator is a substance that acts allosterically by modifying the affinity of a receptor for another transmitter

CRITERIA FOR TRANSMITTER IDENTIFICATION

- Classic criteria for accepting a substance as a transmitter molecule:
    - the substance must be synthesized or stored in the presynaptic cell
    - the substance must be secreted by the presynaptic cell
    - the substance must have postsynaptic effect that duplicates in mechanism the effect of activating the synapse
    - the amount released must be adequate to account for the entire postsynaptic effect
    - an antagonist that blocks the action of the substance must also block the postsynaptic potential
    - substances that satisfy some but not all of the above criteria are referred to as "transmitter candidates"

ELECTRONIC SYNAPSES
- Synapses that use a single transmitter have a synaptic delay of approximately a millisecond
    - in a few systems that require very fast transmission, chemical transmission is bypassed completely
    - a direct connection is made between the pre and the postsynaptic cells
    - these synapses are called electronic synapses or gap junctions

Lecture Topics:

1. The notion that inhibition is more important in the brain than excitation can lead to some interesting topics. For example, might a more intelligent individual have more inhibition than a less intelligent one? How might the concepts of excitation and inhibition relate to intelligence and thought?

2. What evolutionary advantages or disadvantages can the students see in a plant producing a product that is reinforcing or even addictive to animals?

3. The concept of negative feedback and rate-limiting enzymes in the production of transmitters leads to some interesting topics. An example would be an individual who consumes amino acid supplements to increase the levels of various transmitters in brain. Given what the students now know about transmitter synthesis, what would the students recommend about purchasing these products?

Overhead Transparencies:

1. Figure 5-1: Depolarizing and Hyperpolarizing Postsynaptic Potentials.

2. Figure 5-3: Summation and Integration.

3. Figure 5-7: The Structure of the Nicotinic Acetylcholine Receptor.

4. Figure 5-10: Ligands: Agonists and Antagonists.

5. Figure 5-18: The GABA Receptor (Chloride-conducting).

Classroom Demonstrations/Student Activities:

1. Now that the students understand the nature of chemcal transmission, have them perform a frightening exercise. In small groups or as a whole, have them design drugs that would be effective "nerve gases" based on their actions. Once a list has been generated, assign the groups (or class) to do research and find drugs that already exist that perform the functions they described.

Handouts:

1. Table 5-1: Partial List of Known Neuropeptides.

Video List:

Drugs and the Nervous System. Indiana University. Explores the adverse effects of drugs (amphetamines, cocaine, barbiturates, alcohol, opiates, marijuana, PCP, and LSD) on the nervous system.

CHAPTER 6: THE AUTONOMIC NERVOUS SYSTEM

Chapter Outline:

DUAL INNERVATION
- Each target organ has contact with two types of neurons that have different, generally opposing, actions, and distinct transmitter chemistry

Sympathetic Division of the ANS
- One set of neurons innervating the target organs contains norepinephrine as the dominant transmitter type
  - -because the catecholamines are related to each other biosynthetically, the sympathetic system also has some dopamine, and in some places norepinephrine

Parasympathetic Division of the ANS
- The other set of fibers innervating the target organs contains acetylcholine as the dominant transmitter type
  - -like the sympathetic system, the parasympathetic system uses a number of peptide cotransmitters
  - -vasoactive intestinal peptide (VIP) is a probable cotransmitter in some parasympathetic neurons

ANATOMY
- The sympathetic and parasympathetic systems can be distinguished anatomically
  - -the sympathetic ganglia lie adjacent to the spinal column in the paravertebral chain
  - -the parasympathetic ganglia lie in locations that are remote from the CNS

Preganglionic Fibers
- Preganglionic fibers emerge from the CNS to convey motor commands to the nerve cells in the ganglia
  - -in the sympathetic system the preganglionic fibers are short, since they arise in the spinal cord and connect to the paravertebral chain adjacent to the cord
  - -the parasympathetic preganglionic fibers are long, since they must reach the target organs where the parasympathetic ganglia are located

Postganglionic Fibers
- The fibers that emerge from autonomic ganglia are called postganglionic fibers

-sympathetic postganglionics are long since they must extend from the paravertebral chain to the target organ
-parasymapthetic postganglionics are short as the ganglia are typically located near the target organ
-the preganglionics for the sympathetic system all originate from the middle of the spinal cord
- the preganglionics for the parasympathetic system all originate from the top and bottom of the spinal cord

RECEPTORS

- There are two autonommic synapses to consider, the one connecting the preganglionic cell to the postganglionic cell, and the one connecting the postganglionic cell to the target organ

Preganglionic Synapses

- Both the synpathetic and parasympathetic systems use acetylcholine as the transmitter connecting the preganglionics to the ganglia
    -the receptor subtype is the nicotinic cholinergic, the same one used by the somatic neuromuscular junction

Postganglionic Synapses

- The postganglionic fibers of the sympathetic division contain primarily norepinephrine, while those of the parasympathetic system use acetylcholine
    -norepinephrine receptors can be divided into alpha-adrenergic and beta-adrenergic
    -the actions of the two systens are generally antagonistic to each other; if the sympathetic receptor is excitatory, the tissue will express an inhibitory parasympathetic receptor
    -most of the time there is a balance between symapthetic and parasympathetic activity

NONSYNAPTIC RELEASE

- In some cases the autonomic postganglionic contact is a true synapse
    -often, however, the contact is a looser network of terminals called a plexus
    -the site of release at such a network is called a varicosity
    -each varicosity contains electron-rich vesicles that contain the catecholamine transmitter, along with other substances such as dopamine-beta-hydroxylase
    -varicosities also contain dense-cored vesicles, the function of which is currently debated

-fibers that form a nerve plexus tend to be small and
unmyelinated, thus slow

Second and Third Messengers

- The action of transmitters is sometimes slow because there are
sometimes several steps between the ligand binding to the
receptor and the biological effect
    - the receptors for autonomic transmitters lack channels
    altogether
    - the channel affected lies elsewhere in the membrane
    - a complex chain of enzymatically catalyzed events takes
    place inside the cell
    - the autonomic receptors are therefore enzymes, not channels
    - one example of these events is acetylcholine binding to the
    muscarinic receptor
    - the enzyme associated with the muscarinic receptor is called
    a G protein
    - when acetylcholine binds to the receptor, the G protein
    activates a second enzyme, phospholipase C
    - phospholipase C breaks up some phospholipid called
    phosphatidylinositol biphosphate (PIP2) into inositol
    triphosphate, and diacylglycerol (DAG)
    - PIP2 and DAG are second messengers, having a wide range of
    actions on intracellular processes
    - acetylcholine can be excitatory or inhibitory, depending on
    both the receptor and the specific G protein involved
    - intracellular signalling systems are related to many
    important and varied brain processes, including vision,
    learning, and cell development

THE ADRENAL GLAND

- The adrenal glands sit directly on top of the kidneys, and make
adrenaline (epinephrine) from norepinephrine
    - the enzyme phenylethanolamine N-methyltransferase (PNMT)
    makes epinephrine from norepinephrine
    - the adrenal gland is like a large sympathetic ganglia,
    receiving cholinergic innervation and secreting its products
    directly into the bloodstream
    - most of the targets of the adrenal gland receive sympathetic
    innervation, and most of their receptors have overlapping
    affinity for epinephrine and norepinephrine

The Fight-or-Flight Response

- The state of arousal in response to danger is called the fight-or-
flight response

-the body is prepared for physical emergencies
-changes of the fight-or-flight response include heart rate increases, lung airway dilation, glucose release, and pupillary constriction
-many specialists in behavioral medicine believe that the fight-or-flight response may be currently maladaptive, and may be related to disorders like hypertension

Transmitters, Hormones, and Everything in Between

- The body possesses a continuum of chemical signaling mechanisms, including neurotransmitters, neurohormones, hormones, and pheromones
    -the complexity of membrane proteins reflects the degree of specificity demanded of them
    -voltage-gated ion channels share sequence homology, and are composed of a single strand of protein that crosses the membrane many times
    -ligand-gated channels tend to be made up of polymers of separate proteins, each polymer crossing the membrane many times
    -receptors expressed by autonomic targets are made up of a different family of homologous proteins
    -these receptors typically are single strands that span the membrane seven times, but are not attached to channels directly
    -this last family of receptors are called G protein-coupled receptors
    -the ion channel is another protein, called the G protein-linked channel
    -examples of this kind of receptor are the muscarinic, dopamine, serotonin, and numerous peptides

Glucose Mobilization

- Glucose mobilization is an example of a hormonally interacting with a   G protein-coupled receptor
    -the adrenal hormone epinephrine has effects on hepatocytes (liver cells)
    -each hepatocyte expresses beta-adrenergic receptors
    -beta-adrenergic receptors interact with G proteins which activate an enzyme called adenylate cyclase
    -adenylate cyclase catalyzes the production of cyclic adenosine monophosphate (cAMP) from ATP
    -cAMP activates protein kinase which adds phosphate groups to its substrate, phosphorylase kinsase

-each phosphorylase kinase adds a phosphate to its substrate, glycogen phosphorylase
-glycogen phosphorylase acts on glycogen to produce free glucose
-chemical messengers are often used to perform tasks more complex than opening or closing a channel
-the cAMP/protein kinase system amplifies the "dim" message of the hormone

HOW "AUTONOMIC" IS IT?
- The body is constantly experiencing a tension or balance between sympathetic and parasympathetic tone
    -occasions of sympathetic dominance are associated with arousal
    -most situations of sympathetic dominance have a volitional component (e.g., bungee jumping)
    -autonomic functions can proceed without our awareness
    -whether awareness can increase our control of autonomic function is an important and controversial question

THE SPECIAL CASE OF SEX
- Male reproductive function is a classic example of the two systems working in concert with each other
    -erections are produced by parasympathetic activity, while ejaculations are produced by sympathetic activity
    -the genitalia are innervated by tiny sympathetic ganglia that lie in the innervated organ, not in the paravertebral chain

THE SENSORY COMPONENT
- Many autonomic nerves are not motor but sensory
    -sensation from the viscera is mostly pain information, called nociception

"Referred Pain"
- The autonomic sensory fibers join with fibers of the somatic system and then enter the spinal cord
    -thus fusion leads to confusion about visceral and somatic function in the CNS
    -referred pain is sometimes perceived as arising from the body surface instead of from within
    -an example is angina pectoris, perceived pain in the left arm and shoulder that is caused by insufficient oxygen to the heart

-migraine headaches may be due to referred pain from blood vessels in the head

THE ENTERIC NERVOUS SYSTEM AND OTHER SIMPLE SYSTEMS
- The gut has intrinsic networks of sensory and motor fibers that function independently of the CNS and autonomic innervation
   -the sympathetic ganglia that innervate the gut are remote from the paravertebral chain and are part of the enteric nervous system

TRANSMITTERS COMMON TO THE ANS AND CNS
- The major autonomic transmitters, norepinephrine and acetylcholine, also turn up in the brain with their major receptor types

Modes of Action
- Both autonomic transmitters have been implicated in a number of behaviors
   -slices of rat hippocampus let us mimic the "simple systems" approach
   -in this preparation, acetylcholine appears to act on muscarinic receptors, and noprepinephrine appears to act on beta-adrenergic receptors, as in the periphery
   -however, the two transmitters effects on hippocampal neurons are both inhibitory, as opposed to their opposite effects in the periphery
   -each appears to shut down a calcium-activated potassium channel that allows the cells to fire more action potentials

Autoreceptors
- The presynaptic structure also expresses receptors for the transmitter released, called autoreceptors
   -the autoreceptors are generally different receptors than the ones expressed postsynaptically
   -an example is an excitatory postsynaptic beta-adrenergic receptor and an inhibitory presynaptic alpha-adrenergic receptor

Turnover and Breakdown
- Turnover and breakdown of neurotransmitters are the sources of yet more differences between transmitters
   -norepinephrine, for example, is sometimes taken up intact by the presynaptic cell and packaged for rerelease without being degraded

-many drugs that act on the autonomic system affect turnover or breakdown of the transmitters

-cocaine, for example, blocks the re-uptake mechanism for dopamine and norepinephrine

-viagra inhibits the breakdown of the third messenger in the penis and leads to longer erections

Peptide Action in Gut and Brain

- Peptides in the autonomic nervous system also generally have been found in the brain

  -examples include VIP, insulin, and glucagon

Lecture Topics:

1. Students will be familiar with the stories of Zen masters and such who can slow their heart rates down to very few beats per minute. Are these stories true, and if so what do they say about the "autonomic" nervous system?

2. The computer model of the brain has been popular and most students should be familiar with it. This model fits nicely into systems where transmitters bind to receptors and cause depolarizations or hyperpolarizations. How well does it handle systems where second, third, or fourth messengers are involved?

3. Every student will know someone who is taking a drug to lower blood pressure. This can lead to an excellent discussion of stress, the "maladaptiveness" of the stress response, and the influence of personality on health.

Overhead Transparencies:

1. Figure 6-3: Parasympathetic and Sympathetic Ganglia.

2. Figure 6-8: Second and Third Messengers.

3. Figure 6-9: The Synthesis of Catecholamine.

4. Figure 6-12: Glucose Mobilization by Epinephrine.

5. Figure 6-16: Autoreceptors.

Classroom Demonstrations/Student Activities:

1. To demonstrate the power of the sympathetic system, have students first find their resting pulse rate. Then lead them through an exercise where they actively visualize being mugged, chased, etc. Try to get full participation. Then have them take their pulse rate again immediately after the exercise. If they have really tried to participate, their rates should be increased. This can lead to a number of topics including stress, the power of the sympathetic nervous system, and psychosomatic illness.

Handouts:

1. Table 6-1: The Synapses of the Autonomic Nervous System.

Video List:

Psychobiology of Stress. Insight Media. How the brain controls the stress response through nervous, hormonal, and adrenal regulation.

CHAPTER 7: THE SPINAL CORD

Chapter Outline:

A FUNCTIONAL SEGREGATION
- Sensory fibers conveying information towards the CNS are called afferent fibers, motor fibers conveying information from the CNS are called efferents
    -afferent and efferent are also used to describe projections to (afferent) and from (efferent) various parts of the CNS that are not strictly sensory or motor

Orientation
- Anatomy requires many axes of orientation and much spatial reasoning to understand well
    -towards the tip of the head is rostral, towards the tip of the tail is caudal
    -the upper surface of the body is dorsal, the bottom surface is ventral
    -in humans, anterior is sometimes used in place of rostral, and posterior is used in place of caudal
    -medial means close to the midline, and lateral means farther from it
    -proximal means close, and distal means far
    -the thirty-one spinal nerves split into dorsal and ventral the roots
    -the boundary between the CNS and the PNS is the dura mater
    -dorsal roots are primarily sensory, and ventral roots are primarily motor
    -cell bodies for all sensory cells entering the cord lie outside the CNS in a chain of ganglia called the dorsal root ganglia
    -long spinal nerves from the caudal segments dangle down to innervate the legs and are called the cauda equina
    -a local anesthetic can be injected directly into the cauda equina and eliminate the pain of childbirth

Gray Matter and White Matter
- Some CNS tissue is translucent to light and thus appears gray, other areas are opaque to light and thus appear white
    -white matter is myelinated axons, unmyelinated structures comprise gray matter
    -a bundle of axons in the CNS is a tract, fasciculus, or pathway

-gray matter occupies the central region of the spinal cord, surrounding the central canal, an extension of the brain's ventricular system

-the white matter of the spinal cord consists of the sensory afferents and motor efferents

Dermatomes

- Many organisms, such as earthworms, are obviously segmented

    -vertebrates, including people, are also segmented

    -there are thirty-one dermatomes corresponding to the thirty-one spinal nerves

    -each dermatome corresponds to the portion of the body innervated by one set of spinal nerves

    -shingles, a minor yet frightening disease, illustrates that we are indeed segmented organisms

    -the deramtomes can be grouped into categories, rostral to caudal

    -there are first 8 cervical segments, then 12 thoracis segments, then 5 lumbar segments, and 5 sacral segments

    -there is more white matter as one proceeds rostrally, due to the fact that more rostral areas must also contain all of the information for more caudal areas of the cord

    -the CNS is largely a collection of maps of the body and maps of the outside world

Decussation

- Nerve fibers cross the midline to innervate structures on the other side of the body

    -the left brain therefore controls the right side of the body and vice versa

    -when a projection crosses, it is called contralateral, and when it stays on the same side it is ipsilateral

SENSORY PATHWAYS

- In the first stages of processing, synaptic connections are systematic and hierarchical

    -the first cell in sensory sytems is the first-order neuron

    -the soma of all first-order neurons lies outside the CNS in the dorsal root ganglia

    -the first-order neuron synapses onto a second-order neuron, which is in the CNS for somatosensory systems

    -the second-order neuron synapses onto a third-order neuron, etc.

    -the sequences are pretty well understood up to the fourth or fifth-order neurons

Projection of Large Mechanoreceptors
- Sensation from the body surface is of several types
    -slowly conducting fibers are preferentially activated by noxious stimuli
    -large, quickly conducting fibers (mechanoreceptors) handle all of the other somatosensory systems
    -the first order mechanoreceptors enter the cord and ascend ipsilaterally without synapsing
    -two stout bundles arise on either side of the body, the fasciculus gracilis and the fasciculus cuneatus (together called the dorsal columns)
    -these cells connect with the second order cells in the brainstem in the nucleus gracilis and the nucleus cuneatus
    -the third-order neurons are in the thalamus

Projection of Small Nociceptors
- The small diameter, unmyelinated fibers convey information regarding tissue damage into the cord
    -these tiny fibers are not called pain fibers, but rather nociceptors
    -the likely transmitter in first-order nociceptors is Substance P
    -the first-order cell bodies are in the dorsal root ganglia
    -these fibers synapse immediately onto the second-order neuron, which is located in the dorsal horn of the cord
    -the axons of the second-order cells ascends to the brainstem in the lateral spinothalamic tract
    -the third-order cells are located in the thalamus and reticular formation

MOTOR PATHWAYS
- The origin for motor commands lies mysteriously in the cerebral cortex
    -the final common path for motor commands to the body is found in the ventral roots of the spinal cord
    -the lower motor neuron is the neuron that exits the CNS to innervate the skeletal muscles
    -the upper motor neuron, entirely within the CNS, is the cell that contacts the lower motor neuron

Lower Motor Neurons
- The cell bodies for all of the lower motor neurons lie in the gray matter of the ventral horn of the spinal cord

-their axons exit the cord via the ventral roots, and synapse only on skeletal muscle

-they are exclusively cholinergic, nicotinic, and excitatory in nature

-a motor neuron and the cells it contacts are collectively a motor unit

-an excitatory end plate potential results in muscle tissue in response to acetylcholine

-T-tubules in the plasma membrane of muscle carry the regenerating action potential into the cell

-the depolarization liberates stored calcium from the sarcoplasmic reticulum

-the increase in calcium causes a myosin to consume ATP

-the energy provided by ATP causes thick myosin filaments to to pull on thin filaments of actin

-the sliding of actin filaments into myosin causes the muscle to twitch

-electric fish have spinal motor neurons that contact onto specialized electric organs, which have provided us with much information

Upper Motor Neurons

- The brain uses two stout bundles, the pyramidal tracts and the extrapyramidal tracts, to activate lower motor neurons

    -lower motor neurons receive both excitatory and inhibitory contacts from upper motor neurons

    -the excitatory contacts are likely glutamate or aspartate, the inhibitory ones glycine or GABA

- The Pyramidal System is the simpler of the two upper motor neuron pools

    -the lower motor neuron has its cell body in the spinal cord and the upper motor neuron has its cell body in the frontal lobe of the cortex

    -the pyramidal tracts are contralateral, crossing the midline at the decussation of the pyramids

    -most lower motor neurons are innervated by both pyramidal and extrapyramidal neurons

- The extrapyramidal system has not one source but many

    -a number of extrapyramidal systems cluster in the medial ventral part of the white matter of the cord

    -some extrapyramidal projections are ipsilateral

The "Intermediate" Horn

- In the gray matter of the thoracic spinal cord a small enlargement exists between dorsal and ventral horn
    -this is where the cell bodies for the preganglionic sympathetic cells are located

INTEGRATIVE CIRCUITS IN THE CORD
- The spinal cord is not simply a relay between the brain and the body, but has its own capacity to integrate afferent input into appropriate output
    -much integration of stimuli and responses occurs at the level of the spinal cord

Spinal Behaviors
- Some behaviors that the spinal cord can organize on its own are certain sexual behaviors
    -animals with complete spinal transections will still show erection and ejaculation
    -a large component of locomotion is also spinal

The Monosynaptic Reflex
- Each muscle of the body has sensory structures in it and is innervated by lower motor neurons
    -one such sensory structure is the muscle spindle organ
    -extrafusal muscle fibers make up the bulk of muscle and do the majority of the work
    -intrafusal muscle fibers contain a stretch receptor
    -when the intrafusal fibers are stretched, it synapses onto a lower motor neuron that innervates the extrafusal fiber of the same muscle, causing them to contract
    -since only one synapse is involved, it is the monosynaptic reflex
    -any stretch of a muscle is therefore countered with a contraction of that same muscle

Inhibition of Antagonist Muscles
- Every muscle in the body has a monosynaptic reflex
    -muscles exist in antagonistic pairs of flexors and extensors
    -another circuit exists that blocks the antagonist monosynaptic reflex
    -for voluntary movement to occur, one circuit must dominate the other, excitation of the consticting muscle and inhibition of the antagonist

Alpha- and Gamma-Activation
- The lower motor neuron pool can be divided into two types, alpha and gamma motor neurons

-alpha motor neurons contact the extrafusal muscle directly and gamma motor neurons contact the intrafusal muscle directly

-the gamma motor contact is also cholinergic, nicotinic, and excitatory

-both alpha and gamma neruons are involved in voluntary movement

The Renshaw Cell

- Each lower motor neuron sends off an axon collateral within the CNS

    -this collateral makes a central contact with a Renshaw cell

    -the Renshaw cell makes an inhibitory synapse back onto the motor neuron and other motor neurons in the vicinity

    -thus a motor neuron which has just fired is inhibited, as well as all other nearby neurons

    -this is an example of efference copy, a neural memo that a desired motor function has been executed

    -the Renshaw cell is also an example of surround inhibition, a ubiquitous brain process, allowing the brain to maximize contrast

Experimental Research

- Much of the research discussed was conducted on "lower" organisms such as squids or frogs

Lecture Topics:

1. G. Gordon Liddy, one of the Watergate burglars, used to amaze people by putting his hand into the flame from a lighter and leaving it there. Aside from the comment that makes about Mr. Liddy's mental state, it is a good example of how descending pathways can inhibit spinal reflexes, if the individual so chooses.

2. Box 7-3 on animal rights can serve as a good stimulator of discussion. Is it ethical to do experiments on animals, no matter how informative they may be? What if absolutely no pain is caused in the animal?

3. What is the need for two descending motor control systems? Why are both the pyramidal and extrapyramidal systems necessary?

Overhead Transparencies:

1. Figure 7-4: Cross Sections of the Spinal Cord.

2. Figure 7-5: Dermatomes.

3. Figure 7-6: The First-Order Somatosensory Cell.

4. Figure 7-9: The Motor Unit.

5. Figure 7-10: Spinal Circuit #1: The Monosynaptic Reflex.

Classroom Demonstrations/Student Activities:

1. Identify a student with a good patellar reflex. Have them come to the front of the class and reliably produce the reflex. Then ask them to try to inhibit the reflex simply by concentrating. It is a good example of descending information inhibiting spinal reflexes.

Handouts:

1. Figure 7-2: Spinal Cord.

Video List:

The Biology of Behavior. Insight Media. An overview of the human nervous system, showing its components.

CHAPTER 8: FUNCTIONAL ANATOMY OF THE BRAIN

Chapter Outline:

ORIENTATION
- Structures lie on an imaginary line called the neuraxis, with the caudal tip of the spinal cord at one end and the tip of the nose at the other
    -in bipeds, the neuraxis is bent 90 degrees where the spinal cord leaves the brain

GROSS SUBDIVISIONS OF THE BRAIN
- The most caudal portion of the brain, contiguous with the spinal cord, is the brainstem
    -the principal structures of the brainstem are the medulla, pons, and cerebellum
    -the forebrain, which contains the two cerebral hemispheres, makes up the bulk of the brain in humans
    -the forebrain is divided into cortex and subcortical structures
    -at the core of the subcortical structures is the thalamus, an extension of the brainstem
    -the hypothalamus is ventral to the thalamus, and the remainder of forebrain structures are comprised of a group of subcortical structures called the basal ganglia
    -the cortex is divided into frontal, parietal, temporal, and occipital lobes
    -the limbic lobes are subcortical, and include the olfactory bulbs, olfactory cortex, cingulate gyrus, hippocampus and amygdala

Cranial Nerves
- The portions of the body including the face and neck are called brachial segments, and are innervated by twelve cranial nerves
    -the cranial nerves mediate somatosensory function of the head and neck, as well as motor functions of this region
    -the olfactory nerve (I) brings information in about smell and odor into the brain
    -the optic nerve (II) is also purely sensory, and projects contralaterally to the thalamus and brainstem
    -cranial nerves III (oculomotor), IV (trochlear), and VI (abducens) are grouped together and all control eye movements

-the trigeminal nerve (V) has a mixed function, relaying sensations from the face and neck and also controlling the muscles for chewing

-temporal-mandibular joint (TMJ) pain arises from irritation of the trigeminal nerve

-the facial nerve (VII) carries most of the motor innervation for the face

-the acoustic nerve (VIII) relays information from the cochlea about hearing, but also from the vestibular apparatus about balance

-the glossopharyngeal nerve (IX) controls the muscles for swallowing and vocalization, and relays sensory information from the posterior third of the tongue

-the vagus nerve (X) is parasympathetic for most of the internal organs of the body

-the accessory nerve (XI) controls the muscles of the neck

-the hypoglossal nerve (XII) is also purely motor and controls the musces of the tongue

-motorcycle syndome, often seen in accidents, results from tearing and breaking of sensory and motor rootlets in the area where the spinal cord exits the skull, called the foramen magnum

Brainstem

- The tendency for dorsal structures to remain sensory and ventral structures to remain motor breaks down in the pons

    -the pons is really composed of two regions, the pontine nuclei related to primitive brainstem function and the cerebellar peduncles composed of nuclei and fiber tracts

    -more rostrally, the tectum is sensory

    -the superior colliculi are visual, while the inferior colliculi are auditory

    -ventral to the tectum is the substantia nigra, an important brainstem projection to the forebrain of the extrapyramidal motor system

    -the cranial nerve nuclei are intimately associated with each other and mediate a number of reflexes, including the vestibulo-ocular reflex

BRAINSTEM PROJECTIONS TO FOREBRAIN

- The brainstem is densely packed with all the nuclei and fiber tracts that make up the central portion of cranial nerve function, as well as the pons and cerebellum

-the neural "traffic" is so heavy in the region of the pons that early anatomists called it the reticular formation
-the reticular formation also contains three groups of cells that project to the forebrain

Raphe Nuclei
- The raphe nuclei straddle the midsagittal line of the neuroaxis in the pons and medulla
    -the raphe nuclei contain serotonin, and are the primary source of serotonin for the brain and spinal cord
    -the raphe nuclei project caudally to spinal cord, as well as diffusely throughout the brain

Locus Coeruleus
- The locus coeruleus, meaning blue spot, is a tiny structure on either side of the dorsal pons
    -the locus coeruleus is the primary source of norepinephrine for the brain
    -the adrenergic cells project all throughout the cortex and subcortical structures

Substantia Nigra
- The substantia nigra, or black substance, is in the tegmentum of the ventral brainstem
    -the substantia nigra is a major source of dopamine for the brain, and projects to basal ganglia structures important in extrapyramidal motor behavior
    -another dopamine projection terminates in the limbic medial forebrain bundle and appears to play a role in reward systems

BASAL GANGLIA
- The basal ganglia is a group of structures comprised of the caudate nucleus, the putamen, and the globus pallidus, and associated with the amygdala and pulvinar nucleus of the thalamus
    -another name for the region is the corpus striatum, because of the striped appearance
    -blood vessels in the region are small and thus are susceptible to occlusions or ruptures, leading to a interruption of blood supply (stroke)

LIMBIC SYSTEM
- The limbic system is an amalgam of structures that can also be assigned to other systems, and has a role in "primitive" functions

-the limbic system is composed of the amygdala, mammillary bodies, olfactory bulbs and nuclei, septum, hippocampus, and habenula

-bundles of axons such as the stria terminalis, fornix, stria medullaris, and the medial forebrain bundle connect limbic structures

HYPOTHALAMUS AND PITUITARY

- On the ventral surface of the forebrain is a midline cluster of nuclei and a gland hanging down

   -the nuclei of the hypothalamus receive diverse input and send infomation to the pituitary gland via the infundibulum

   -the pituitary secretes peptide hormones with diverse functions

   -some peptides are released into the blood from axon tips in the posterior lobe of the pituitary, where the cell bodies are in the hypothalamus itself

   -the anterior pituitary also releases hormones and is controlled by neural input from the hypothalamaus

THALAMUS

- The most central structure in the forebrain is the thalamus, an "old brain" region that communicates with the brainstem

   -the thalamus can be thought of as the location where the cortex communicates with the brainstem

<u>Relay Nuclei</u>

- Some thalamic nuclei receive specific projections from brainstem systems and project in turn to discrete regions of cortex

   -when these can be associated with a specific sensory modality, they are called relay nuclei

   -the lateral geniculate nuclei relay visual information, the medial geniculate nuclei relay auditory information, and the ventralposterior lateral nuclei and ventral posterior medial nuclei relay somatosensory information

<u>Association Nuclei</u>

- Other thalamic nuclei cannot be assigned a simple sensory or motor modality, and are thus called association nuclei

   -the distinction between relay and association nuclei may reflect more our lack of current knowledge, rather than fundamental differences between them

NEOCORTEX

- The bulk of the human brain consists of two heavily convoluted hemispheres, collectively called the neocortex
    - the neocortex can be divided into frontal, parietal, temporal, and occipital lobes, which perform different functions
    - the hemispheres are made up of units called columns that have intrinsic circuitry and projection fibers
    - the columns also have discrete layers, which in vertebrates are six in number
    - afferent projections terminate in layer IV, and efferent projections originate from layers V and VI
    - layer I consists of white matter, while layers II and III consist of intrisic or local circuit cells

Primary Cortex

- Primary cortex is cortex that receives a direct projection from thalamic relay nuclei and has a large layer IV to accommodate all the afferents
    - motor cortex has a pronounced layer V and VI to accommodate all of the motor neuron cell bodies

Association Cortex

- Association cortex, between the two extremes of sensory and motor cortex, tends to communicate with thalamic association nuclei and other cortical regions

Temporal Lobes

- The temporal lobes, on the side of the brain near the temples, are separated from the other lobes of the cortex by the lateral sulcus.
    - in this sulcus is the primary auditory cortex, receiving input from the medial geniculate nucleus

Occipital Lobes

- The caudal tip of the skull is the occiput, and the lobes underneath are the occipital lobes
    - in the occipital lobe is the primary visual cortex which receives input from the lateral geniculate nucleus

Parietal Lobes

- Caudal to the central sulcus are the parietal lobes
    - the postcentral gyrus, the first gyrus caudal to the central sulcus, is the primary somatosensory cortex

Frontal Lobes

- All cortex rostral to the central sulcus is considered part of the frontal lobes
    - the precentral gyrus, immediately rostral to the central sulcus, constitutes the primary motor cortex

-the rostral pole of the frontal lobes probably plays a role in ideation and cognition and was the part separated from the rest of the brain in a prefrontal lobotomy
-the frontal lobes are larger and more elaborate in humans than in other primates

OTHER NEOCORTEX

- Not all cortex can be neatly categorized as belonging to one of the four lobes
    -some structures, such as hippocampus, give the appearance of cortex but have fewer than six layers
    -these cortical regions are grouped with the limbic lobes
    -several stout pathways, called commisures, connect the hemispheres, the largest of which is the corpus callosum

VENTRICLES

- In the center of the brain and through the core of the spinal cord are fluid-filled chambers called the ventricles and central canal
    -there are two large ventricles on either side of the cerebral hemispheres called the lateral ventricles
    -a smaller ventricle in the center is the third ventricle, and more caudally is the fourth ventricle
    -the fluid in the ventricles is cerebrospinal fluid, very similar to blood plasma, and manufactured in the choroid plexus

MENINGES AND THE BLOOD-BRAIN BARRIER

- The entire brain and cord are enveloped by membranes that insulate the CNS from mechanical disturbances
    -close to the CNS is the pia mater and arachnoid membranes, separated by blood vessels and CSF
    -beneath the bone is a tough leathery membrane called the dura mater
    -the blood vessels of the brain are insulated from brain tissue by an elaborate membrane called the blood-brain barrier (BBB)
    -the BBB is hydrophobic, and isolates the brain from perturbations in blood chemistry

TRACT-TRACING TECHNIQUES AND STEREOTAXY

- Two general approaches have been used to acquire knowledge of brain connections
    -since CNS tissue does not regenerate, creating a lesion destroys a cluster of neurons but also destroys distal

structures such as axons and boutons, called orthograde degeneration

-degeneration in the other direction, from the axon back to the cell body, is called retrograde degeneration

-refinements of these techniques allow the origin and destination of fiber tracts to be determined without lesions

-stereotaxy is the placement of electrodes into a brain to stimulate or record activity

Lecture Topics:

1. The idea that interspecies differences in brain size causes differences in cognitive ability is well established. Differences in human intellect must be in the brain somewhere, but not as gross size differences. What are some of the possible sites or differences betweeen the brains of people with different cognitive abilities?

2. The very diffuse projections of norepinephrine and serotonin can provide interesting lecture material. What could the function of such a diffusely projecting system be? Is it surprising that these transmitters have been implicated in something as global as "mood?"

3. The topic of prefrontal lobotomies can introduce the subject of psychosurgery in general. Will we ever get to the point where very discrete lesions could eliminate problem behaviors in some individuals? If we ever achieve that goal, who gets to decide the appropriate subjects for surgery?

Overhead Transparencies:

1. Figure 8-1: Gross Subdivisions of the Brain.

2. Figure 8-3: Cranial Nerves.

3. Figure 8-7: The Limbic System.

4. Figure 8-9: The Relationship between the Thalamus and the Neocortex.

5. Figure 8-11: Microstructure of Neocortex.

Classroom Demonstrations/Student Activities:

1. Dim the lights to let the students pupils dilate. Let them then take a penlight (not too stong!) and shine it into one of their student colleague's eyes. The pupil of the other eye will constrict because of the consensual pupillary light reflex.

Handouts:

1. Figure 8-1: Gross Subdivisions of the Human Brain.

Video List:

The Brain-Mind Connection. Insight Media. This video explores how the physical attributes of the human brain influence and are influenced by thought, behavior, and the environment.

The Human Brain. Insight Media. The most complex organ in the body, the brain consumes more energy than any other organ and has greater computing ability than one thousand of the world's fastest computers working together.

CHAPTER 9: SENSORY SYSTEMS

Chapter Outline:

SOMATOSENSORY SYSTEMS
- Feelings from the body come from not one, but many, sensory systems
    - pressure from the body surface, vibration of the skin, and deflection of hair on the body surface all contribute to bodily awareness
    - there are even systems, for example proprioceptors, that never reach conscious awareness

Organs of Touch
- Free nerve endings of small myelinated and unmyelinated fibers, are nociceptors and transport information regarding noxious stimli to the CNS
    - tissue damage depolarizes these nociceptors directly
    - sensory terminals for other neurons change physical energy in the form of pressure, stretch, or vibration into neural energy
    - this process is called transduction and the sensory organs that accomplish this for the nerve endings are end organs

Adaptation and Generator Potentials
- Primary sensory neurons do not have dendrites, but neurites which conduct action potentials like axons do
    - transduction of physical energy (pressure, stretch, or vibration) depolarizes the most peripheral patch of excitable membrane
    - this depolarization is called a generator potential, and is graded in amplitude according to the strength of the stimulus
    - the generator potential amplitude is then converted into action potential frequency
    - the universal code for representing intensity is increased frequency of firing
    - generator potentials are also self-terminating, that is they do not exist throughout the duration of the stimulus
    - this phenomenon is called adaptation
    - adaptation is conferred on nerve endings by specialized end organs, such as pacinian corpuscles, and Meissner's, Merkel's, and Ruffini's corpuscles

Central Projections

- The neurites bearing the action potentials arising from somatosensory lead to the dorsal root ganglia
    - the central projections of the mechanoreceptors are remarkably orderly
    - the information entering the cord adds onto the dorsal columns
    - the information ends up in the postcentral gyrus of the parietal lobe as the primary sensory homunculus
    - there are at least five homunculi in human cortex

Proprioceptors and Their Projections

- Some proprioceptors terminate in the cord and participate in circuits that are purely spinal
    - other proprioceptors project rostrally, particularly to brainstem structures like the cerebellum
    - the proprioceptors do not always display adaptation and conscious awareness

AUDITORY SYSTEM

- Tonotopic maps exist in the auditory system that represent the range of frequency of sounds that penetrate the ears
    - pitch is unidimensional, but is mapped onto two dimensions of neural surface

Organs of Hearing

- The ear in mammals consists of three parts
    - the visible portion is the pinna, which are flaps of skin and cartilage that focus sound waves on the sensitive parts of the ear
    - the eardrum or tympanic membrane separates the outer from the middle ear
    - vibrations in the air cause cause compression of the tympanic membrane, which moves the first of three tiny bones, the malleus (mallet)
    - the malleus hammers into the incus (anvil), which vibrates the stapes (stirrup)
    - these bones deform a membrane called the oval window, which separates the air-filled middle ear from the fluid-filled inner ear
    - a membrane at the other end of the inner ear, the round window, is caused by deformations of the sound window
    - the inner ear is made up of the cochlea and the vestibular apparatus

-the scala media is a fluid-filled chamber in the middle of the cochlea
-within the scala media is a stiff, resonant structure called the basilar membrane is where the neurons that transduce sound exist
-sound causes a wave of motion that penetrates down the basilar membrane to varying degrees depending on the frequency of the sound
-the primary sensory cells for audition are called hair cells
-the membrane potential oscillates at precisely the frequency of the sound that comes in

Hindbrain Projections

- The hair cells lack axons and fire no action potentials
    -the second-order cells send a dendrite to receive the oscillating synaptic transmission from the hair cells
    -for low frequency cells at the apex of the cochlea, action potential frequency matches the sound frequency
    -however, action potentials cannot match sounds higher then 5,000 HZ (cycles per second)
    -at higher frequencies, a volley principle is employed, meaning that associated cells fire in different parts of the cycle and represent pitch
    -amplitude is represented by each auditory cell having a tuning curve, each having a different frequency/amplitude relation based on the cell's place in the tonotopic map
    -the second-order auditory neuron projects through the eigth cranial nerve to the dorsal and ventral cochlear nucleus
    -from there, there is a divergence of projections to higher-order cells including the superior olive and the inferior colliculus

Thalamic and Cortical Projections

- Auditory fibers from the inferior colliculus project to the medial geniculate nucleus (MGN) of the thalamus, and then to the primary auditory cortex in the temporal lobe
    -the second dimension of neural surface is used to compute the location of a sound source

Efferent Projections

- Efferent projections also exist from higher-order cells back down to lower-order cells.
    -the CNS continually filters and processes auditory information, eliminating undesirable signals and enhancing important ones

Vestibular System and Its Projections

- The senses of balance and angular movements are often wholly subconscious
    - -the brain determines body position with respect to gravity, using two inner ear structures, the utricle and the saccule
    - -movement of the head in any direction starts a generator potential in hair cells of these structures
    - -the dynamic sense of movement of the head is provided by the semicircular canals on either side of the head

OLFACTION AND GUSTATION
- Taste and smell are very closely related sensory modalities
    - -lack of smell, anosmia, diminishes the savory quality of food
    - -the sensory receptors from smell and taste are chemoreceptors, cells that respond to chemical stimuli

Organs of Taste
- The first-order cells for taste in the taste buds lie in between bulges, called papillae, in the tongue
    - -taste buds produce generator potentials in response to specific chemical stimuli
    - -four types of receptors have been studied extensively, those for bitter, sour, salty, and sweet
    - -bitter tastes arise from the back of the tongue, sweet from the tip of the tongue, sour or salty stimuli seem to employ mechanisms unique to gustation

Organs of Smell
- Primary olfactory cells are neurons called bipolar cells
    - -first-order olfactory cells are capable of firing action potentials
    - -it is unclear how many specific receptor types there are for smell, but smell is probably analogous to taste in that a small number of receptors combines to produce smell sensations

Central Projections
- Cranial nerves VIII, IX, and X bear gustatory signals into the brainstem
    - -the gustatory afferents terminate in the gustatory nucleus
    - -a cortical projection to the thalamus and association parietal cortex probably mediates the conscious aspects of gustation
    - -central olfactory projections go directly to cortical structures, bypassing the brainstem relay nuclei seen in other systems

-the projections go from second-order cells in the olfactory bulbs to diverse destinations including the anterior olfactory nuclei, the olfactory tubercle, the pyriform cortex, and limbic regions like central amygdaloid nucleus and entorhinal area
-there are ultimately thalamic and cortical projections that probably mediate the conscious perception of smell

VISION
- The subject of vision has generated extensive research and understanding
  -a detailed understanding of vision provides a model for all other sensory systems, as well as brain function in general

Anatomy and Circuitry of the Retina
- The lens of the eye inverts the image to the retina like a slide projector inverts a slide.
  -transduction of the visual image occurs in two populations of photoreceptors, called rods and cones
  -rods are responsible for black and white vision, while cones are sensitive to color
  -there are three cone types corresponding to each of the three primary colors
  -the center of the visual field is the fovea, where cones predominate
  -cones synapse onto bipolar cells, with less convergence than rods do, and thus have more spatial resolution
  -rods and cones both have a region of membranous folds called the outer segment, which contains the photopigment
  -rods have more folds than cones, and thus more light sensitivity
  -rods and cones also synapse with horizontal cells, and bipolar cells synapse with ganglion cells
  -ganglion cells are the first cells in the visual system that can fire action potentials
  -a fifth type of cell, the amacrine cell, exists in the inner plexiform layer with the ganglion cells

Transduction of the Light Stimulus
- Embedded in the membrane of the disks of rods is a photopigment called rhodopsin
  -rhodopsin is similar to ligand-activated receptors for some transmitters linked to second-messenger systems
  -the prevailing state of rhodopsin is bound and activated, the condition that exists in the dark

-when a photon strikes retinal bound to rhodopsin, retinal changes shape in a process called photoisomerization, and unbinds from the rhodopsin

-the first step in the visual system of vertebrates is inhibitory, involving the unbinging of a ligand to its receeotor and the inactivation of a second-messenger system active in the dark

Surround Inhibition

- Diffuse illumination of the retina is usually ineffective or weakly effective in eliciting ganglion cell action potentials

    -the receptive fields of ganglion cells were found to contain two parts, one excitatory and one inhibitory

    -the parts invariably consisted of a circle surrounded by a ring

    -cells where the circle was excitatory and the ring was inhibitory were dubbed on cells

    -the ultimate contribution of receptive fields is to create contrast

    -receptive fields are different sizes, and are malleable

    -the perception of contrast is created by horizontal cells

    -the on-center of an on-cell causes excitation of the bipolar cell via hyperpolarizing generator potentials

    -the off-center of an off-cell causes inhibition of the bipolar cell

    -the on-surround of an off-cell causes inhibition of the horizontal cell

    -the off-surround of an off-cell causes the disexcitation of the horizontal cell

    -the vast majority of information leaving the retina consists of dots and circles

    -the eye is a contrast detector, enhancer, and creator

    -local antagonistic influences are common if not ubiquitous in the CNS

Thalamic and Brainstem Projections

- Binocular organisms display partial decussation of visual information

    -the nasal hemiretina sees the lateral field of view and dicussate, the temporal hemiretina sees the medial part of view and do not decussate

    -at the optic chiasm, the optic nerve fibers separate themselves into an ipsilateral (temporal) and a contralateral (nasal) projection

    -the bundle is called the optic tract after the chiasm

-most of the optic nerve in mammals terminates in the superior colliculus
-the colliculus in turn projects back to the oculomotor nuclei and cerebellum to coordinate tracking movements of the eyes
-another projection goes to the lateral geniculate nucleus (LGN) of the thalamus
-the contralateral visual world is mapped in alternating bands in the LGN
-there are two different cell types in the LGN, magnocellular layers concerned with movement detection and parvocellular layers concerned with analysis of color and detail
-the LGN also receives efferent projections from visual cortex whose function is obscure

Cortical Circuits and Columns

- LGN afferents terminate in the primary visual cortex at the occipital pole of the brain
    -the cells that receive the input are in layer IV and also consist of circular receptive fields with antagonistic surrounds
    -Hubel and Wiesel discovered that most cells in visual cortex respond to edges or bars of light of a particular orientation with respect to the retina, called simple cells
    -each half of the visual cortex can be thought of as consisting of bands of cells of particular orientation selectivity
    -there are also alternating bands for each eye's inputs
    -the orientation bands for each eyes input intersect at right angles so for a given portion of cortex there are columns of simple cells that respond to stimulation of one eye in a particular orientation
    -the cortex is best thought of as as consisting of orientation columns and ocular dominance columns
    -two ocular dominance columns (one for each eye) and 180 degrees of orientation columns is a hypercolumn
    -the hypercolumn is the unit of integration at the simple cell level, and the primary visual cortex can be thought of as a mosaic of hypercolumns
    -embedded within each hypercolumn are regions specialized to add color, called blobs
    -there are also complex cells and hypercomplex cells that respond to moving edges, for example

Association Visual Cortex

- Parallel projections from the LGN carry information about depth, color, and motion to the simple cells of the primary visual cortex

-at least three parallel pathways exist that convey processed information to the association visual cortex, and association cortex in other lobes

-one pathway is primarily occupied with color vision, another with depth, form, and color, and the third with motion, depth, and form of stimuli

-at least twenty separate retinotopic maps can be found in areas 18 and 19

Diagnostic Neurology of the Visual System

- The function of very high order visual cortex is hard to evaluate experimentally

  -some of our best information about high order cortex comes from people who have suffered selective damage to portions of the visual system

  -complete damage to one of the optic nerves renders the subject unable to see in that eye

  -lesions to the optic tract produces blindness in the same half of the visual world in each eye

  -after the LGN, fibers in the visual system form a fan-shaped structure called the optic radiation

  -strokes often damage the internal capsule, near the optic radiations, and produce partial paralysis and incomplete hemianopsia

  -if the lesion occurs in the wide fan region of the radiation where much of the neural space is occupied by fibers from the fovea, the condition is called macular sparing which only affects peripheral vision

  -damage to the association visual cortex produce partial blindness in the entire visual world

  -various agnosias can occur including prosopagnosia, the inability to recognize faces

  -lesions to inferotemporal cortex may result in lack of motion perception and/or a difficulty in distinguishing the proper sequence of visual events in time

SIX PRINCIPLES OF SENSORY PHYSIOLOGY

- Sensory systems display adaptation
- Stimulus intensity is encoded by action potential frequency
- There is much modality segregation in sensory systems
- The sensory surface is topographically organized subcortically and cortically
- Receptive fields have antagonistic surrounds

- Sensation is characterized by efferent control over the precept

Lecture Topics:

1. How do the projection pathways of the olfactory system explain why smell is often linked to strong memories and emotions? Every student in the class should have at least one recollection of a perfume, cologne, or other smell triggering an intense memory or emotion.

2. How can it be argued that color does not really exist in the outside world, but is simply a creation of the visual system?

3. Since the entire visual system serves as a contrast detector and even creator, students may wonder about the "accuracy" of their sight. How "good" is our vision if our nervous systems are distorting or even creating information at every level?

Overhead Transparencies:

1. Figure 9-3: The Ear.

2. Figure 9-11: The Tongue and Gustation.

3. Figure 9-12: Organs of Smell.

4. Figure 9-14: The Eye.

5. Figure 9-27: The Circuit for a Simple Cell.

Classroom Demonstrations/Student Activities:

1. Take a willing student and blindfold him or her in the middle of the room, surrounded by their colleagues. Have students clap, one at a time, around the room and have the blindfolded student point to the location of the noise. This demonstration will demonstrate the excellent ability we have to localize sound origins.

Handouts:

1. Six Principles of Sensory Physiology (pp. 226-227).

Video List:

Sensation and Perception. Insight Media. This video explains how human beings construct reality from the raw material provided by the senses and how the brain interprets and organizes this material into meaningful patterns.

The Doors of Perception. Insight Media. Explore the relationship between the internal world of human conscousness and the external world.

CHAPTER 10: MOTOR SYSTEMS

Chapter Outline:

THE FRONTAL AND PARIETAL LOBES
- The frontal lobes are associated primarily with motor function and the parietal lobes are associated primarily with sensory function
    - there is substantial overlap between sensory and motor function at every level

"Psychomotor" Cortex
- We can dissect the impetus for behavior into four stages: motivation, readiness, plan for action, and execution
    - psychomotor cortex is that part of the cortex involved in motor activity
    - the motivation for action arises in the limbic system
    - information about the body's readiness to act most likely arises in portions of the frontal lobe called the premotor cortex and supplementary motor area (SMA), through a projection from the posterior parietal cortex
    - the plan for action appears to arise in the premotor cortex and the SMA
    - the motivation for action very possibly influences the plan for action by a projection to the premotor and SMA by the cingulate gyrus
    - the plan for action is conveyed from the premotor cortex and SMA to the primary motor cortex for execution
    - much of our knowledge of motor physiology has been obtained using humans as research subjects
    - with electroencephalography, it is possible to record a readiness potential in premotor areas that precedes volitional movements by almost a second

The Motor Homunculus
- In the precentral gyrus, the first fold rostral to the central sulcus, lies a map of the body analogous to the somatotopic map of the postcentral gyrus
    - the motor homunculus is oriented across the surface of the brain in a manner just like the somatosensory homunculus
    - the symmetry of sensory and motor structures across the central sulcus is probably not an accident, as other examples exist of sensory-motor communication

Primary Motor Cortex

- Commands from psychomotor cortex are continually refined as they pass caudally toward the lower motor neuron pools
    - recordings taken from upper motor neurons in primary motor cortex appear to confirm that their activity reflects a more general indication of the premotor cortex's plan to move the body
    - a population vector (an expression of the tendency to fire with movement in a particular direction) of a large number of cortical unit records corresponds closely to actual movements
    - only lower motor neurons controlling the digits of the hand are under the direct control of the primary motor cortex
    - in the human brain there are some 30,000 giant pyramidal cells, called Betz cells, in each primary motor cortex
    - these combine with fibers that originate in premotor and somatosensory cortex to form the pyramidal tracts
    - most of the pyramidal tracts decussate to form the lateral corticospinal tracts, some project ipsilaterally in the ventral corticospinal tracts
    - all other motor function in primates is provided by the extrapyramidal system

THE BASAL GANGLIA

- After a decision to act has been made, movement still requires the participation of a group of nuclei in the center of the cerebrum known collectively as the basal ganglia
    - the afferent and efferent projections of the basal ganglia are widespread in thalamus and neocortex
    - the basal ganglia in humans seem prone to a number of diseases, whose symptoms always include inhibition of voluntary movements and initiation of motor movements
    - this seems to indicate that the basal ganglia function in the volitional aspects of motor performance

Caudate, Putamen, and Globus Pallidus

- Innervation of the basal ganglia arises from all cortical areas including primary motor cortex, premotor areas, and frontal association cortex and limbic structures
    - much of the input arises in two nuclei, called the caudate nucleus, and the putamen, together called the striatum
    - the corticostriate projections to the putamen are associated with descending motor commands
    - the striatum projects within the basal ganglia to the globus pallidus

-two structures are associated with the output of the basal ganglia, the subthalamic nucleus and the dopaminergic projection that originates in the substantia nigra

-the output is predominately back to cortex via thalamic motor relays in the ventrolateral nucleus and two other thalamic nuclei, the ventral anterior and mediodorsal

-all of these project back to frontal cortex, suggesting an organizing and integrating function

The Pathobiology of Stroke and Diseases of the Basal Ganglia

- The vascular supply of the internal capsule and striatum consists of arterioles (fine arteries) and venules (fine veins) that are particularly vulnerable to blockage, called a stroke

  -consequences of stroke are loss of blood flow (ischemia), infarct (tissue damage), and hypoxia (inadequate oxygen), or anoxia (absence of oxygen)

  -these events cause cell death which results in hemiplegia, or partial paralysis on the contralateral side of the body

  -there is often a loss of sensory function as well, such as numbness or paresthesia

  -Parkinson's disease and Huntington's disease are two disorders of the basal ganglia

  -Parkinson's is a deficit in the amount of dopamine secreted by the substantia nigra, while Huntington's is a deficit in cells that secrete acetylcholine and GABA

  -Parkinson's disease is characterized by an inability to initiate movement, called akinesia, and a "pill-rolling" tremor

  -L-dopa can be an effective treatment, it is not a cure and can lose effectiveness as the disease proceeds

  -an approach to a cure involves the transplantation of aminergic tissue, although controversy exists about their efficacy

  -a second approach is to identify the disease early in its progress and intervene

  -this second approach entails an understanding of the etiology of the disease which remains elusive

  -Parkinson's may be a result of viral or genetic causes, or a result of a toxin, as evidenced by heroin users who developed symptoms of the disease after accidental ingestion of a neurotoxin

  -Huntington's symptoms are an excess of undesired movements and lack of muscle tone

  -the movments consist of sudden limb movments, called choreas, which are called hemiballismus if they are violent

-Huntington's is a genetic disorder, and there is currently no effective therapy

THE CEREBELLUM

- The connections of the cerebellum suggest a precise, limited influence over the activity of the extrapyramidal system, especially with respect to execution

Afferents

- The phylogenetically oldest part of the cerebellum receives input directly from the vestibular organs and is thus called the vestibulocerebellum
    -it lies most caudally in the flocculonodular lobe
    -the bulk of the human cerebellum is made up of the spinocerebellum
    -the principal input to the spinocerebellum is from proprioceptors in the spinal cord
    -surrounding the spinocerebellum laterally and dorsally is the corticocerebellum
    -the principal input to the corticocerebellum is from extrapyramidal motor cortex

Efferents

- There are three principal outputs from the cerebellum, just as there are three principal inputs
    -the vestibulocerebellum projects back to vestibular structures directly, but all other output flows through intermediate structures known as the deep cerebellar nuclei
    -the spinocerebellum projects inward to the fastigial nucleus and the interposed nucleus, and from there to descending extrapyramidal structures including the red nucleus
    -the outflow of the corticocerebellum is through both sides of the dentate nucleus, which also projects back to the red nucleus, and ultimately back to cortex
    -the output to cortex arrives in SMA and premotor areas and is thought to organize postural adjustments that are necessary to maintain the body in an upright position

Intrinsic Circuitry

- There is a deceptively simple synaptic circuit that lies within each of the three cerebellar divisions
    -the cerebellum has a capacity for vector analysis that surpasses computers
    -the cerebellum has a latticelike organization that uses parallel processing strategies

-the specific inputs arrive in the cerebellar cortex in a type of axon called a mossy fiber
-the cerebellum has not six layers, but three, and the mossy fibers terminate in the deepest of these, called the granular layer because of the predominance of granular cells
-the excitatory mossy fiber input is modified by a local inhibitory cell called a Golgi cell
-the middle layer is called the Purkinje cell layer because the predominant cell type there is the Purkinje cell
-Purkinje cell dendrites extend into the uppermost layer, the molecular layer
-rays of granule cell axons are called parallel fibers because they are parallel to each other
-stellate cells and basket cells focus excitatory activity within the parallel fibers by creating local circuit inhibition in the molecular layer
-Purkinje cells also receive input from climbing fibers, afferents that originate in the brainstem inferior olive
-an interaction between synaptic inputs from parallel fibers and climbing fibers is the actual basis for motor learning
-the cerebellum also receives diffuse projections from noradrenergic and serotinergic fibers that renders the cells more responsive to other synaptic input
-the Purkinje cell is the only cell type that projects axons out of the cerebellar cortex, and these projections are exclusively inhibitory
-cerebellar influence on motor behavior is therefore mediated exclusively by inhibition and disinhibition

THE IMPORTANCE OF INHIBITION
• The output of the cerebellar cortex, Purkinje cells constantly bombarding brainstem motor structures, illustrates the importance of inhibition in the brain

Efference Copy in the Oculomotor System
• The control of movement of the eyes in the orbits has many features in common with other motor systems, but a few that are unique
   -oculomotor neurons lack the monosynaptic reflex and Renshaw circuit of spinal neurons
   -six separate brainstem systems influence the movements of the eyes
   -the first of these is the vestibulo-ocular reflex, involving only three cells and synapses

-the vestibulo-ocular reflex can be modified a number of ways, including the use of glasses
-when both the head and the object of interest is moving, the vestibulo-ocular reflex gives way to the optokinetic reflex, which integrates vestibular and visual input to hold an image stable
-three forms of eye movements track objects when the head is still
-saccades are small darting movements of the eyes
-smooth pursuit involves the maintenance of gaze on a moving object
-vergence movements is the movement of the eyes in different directions, as when tracking an object that is getting closer or farther away
-a sixth projection to the eyes from the third cranial nerve and from the sympathetic ganglia regulates the diameter of the pupil
-there is a nonreflexive aspect to pupillary size related to interest and alertness

Epilepsy and Seizures

- The transmitter GABA is likely to be the mediator of most inhibitory synapses in the brain, and glycine likely mediates most inhibition in the cord
    -GABA or glycine antagonists produce seizures, convulsive unrestrained motor excitation of part or all of the body
    -clinical conditions that have seizures as a symptom are collectively called epilepsy
    -partial or focal epilepsy involve seizures in only part of the body and results from unbounded excitation in a restricted brain region
    -epilepsy has multiple causes, including drug abuse, suicide attempts, and cerebrovascular accidents
    -generalized epilepsy entails seizures involving the entire body
    -petit mal seizures or absence seizures have seizures that are not dramatic or life threatening, but still involve a loss of consciousness
    -grand mal seizures also involve a loss of consciousness but also have forceful muscle constriction causing rigidity (tonus) followed by dramatic jerking movements (clonus)
    -EEG recordings show that grand mal seizures involve a focus of activity in one part of the brain that spreads to the entire brain

COMMAND NEURONS AND MOTOR TAPES

- Study of simple nervous systems can be very illuminating in understanding how action comes about

    -invertebrate nervous systems often display eutely, or the exact same number of neurons in the brain of each member of the species

    -some of the best understood motor networks locomotion and escape behaviors

    -rhythmic behaviors such as locomotion appear to arise from activation of central pattern generators

    -vertebrates don't posess many identifiable neurons, but in fish and amphibians there are a pair of giant fibers, the Mauthner cells, that organize escape behavior

    -the types of behaviors organized by eutelous and hard-wired nervous systems are called fixed action patterns

    -fixed action patterns are released by a sensory stimulus, and play out in a very stereotypic form via a motor tape, activated by command neurons

    -modern ethology finds few true complex behaviors that are as fixed as they would be if they were controlled by motor tapes

    -the development of eutelous systems involves apoptosis, or cell death

    -very likely, the acquisition of skills and abilities also involves the elimination of synapses and neurons

Lecture Topics:

1. The story of Muhammed Ali can provide interesting lecture topics. Ali exhibits classic Parkinsonian symptoms. Could his years of boxing have contributed, exacerbated, or even caused this disease?

2. The treatment of basal ganglia disorders with transplanted tissue raises a number of discussion points. Should we transplant brain tissue at all? Is it ethical to transplant fetal tissue? How would the students' answers change if the likelihood of recovery was 100%? What if it was 20%?

3. Recent data indicate that treating the seizures that occur after brain injuries with anticonvulsants can slow behavioral recovery. Perhaps seizures in this situation serve to help the brain "rewire itself" after an injury and the medical strategy of eliminating them at all times may be incorrect.

Overhead Transparencies:

1. Figure 10-1: Psychomotor Cortex.

2. Figure 10-6: Elements of the Basal Ganglia.

3. Figure 10-7: Divisions of the Cerebellum.

4. Figure 10-9: Circuitry of the Cerebellum.

5. Figure 10-11: Vestibulo-ocular Reflex.

Classroom Demonstrations/Student Activities:

1. Break students into two "teams" to debate the pros and cons of tissue transplantation for neurological disorders such as Parkinson's disease. The debate should enlighten them to the complexities of transplantation, the ambiguities of the findings, and the ethical problems inherent in the procedure.

Handouts:

1. Figure 10-5: Direction Selectivity in Primary Motor Cortex.

Video List:

Sensory-Motor Integration. Edited clip from "The Mind" series. Describes how sensory and motor systems are integrated.

Brain Transplants in Parkinson's Patients. Edited clip from "The Mind" series. Describes the research examining transplantation of brain tissue in animals and humans.

CHAPTER 11: PLEASURE AND PAIN

Chapter Outline:

THE PROBLEM OF DEFINITIONS
- Sensory systems create as actively as they experience stimuli
    -working definitions of pleasure usually include the concept of reward, a stimulus that an animal will work to obtain
    -operational definitions of pain fall into two categories
    -stimuli are defined as noxious if they cause tissue damage
    -the second definition assumes that animals will object to the same things that humans will object to
    -an example is the tail-flick test, a meaure of how fast a rat will flick their tail away from a radiant heat source

IS THERE A "PLEASURE CIRCUIT" IN THE BRAIN?
- There are probably several pleasure circuits in the brain
    -two are well understood, one using dopamine, and the other using a class of peptide transmitters collectively called the endogenous opiates

Self-Stimulation Studies
- In the 1950's, Olds and Milner accidently discovered that electrodes implanted in parts of the brains of rats would lead to the animal performing an operant response to obtain electrical stimulation in that brain region
    -the animals would also display appetitive behaviors while they were being reinforced, but the brain stimulation did not show satiety like appetitive behaviors would

The Medial Forebrain Bundle
- Olds and Milner found many sites in the brain where self-stimulation could be produced
    -one region produced the best self-stimulation and at lower electrical intensities
    -this region was not a nucleus, but rather a fiber tract, the medial forebrain bundle
    -one projection area of the medial forebrain bundle was the nucleus accumbens, which has been the subject of extensive research

Dopamine and Reward Systems
- The cells of origin for the medial forebrain bundle lie in the substantia nigra and ventral tegmentum, two regions of dopamine-containing cell bodies

-the projection from the substantia nigra is called the nigrostriatal pathway because it terminates in the striatum
-the projection from the ventral tegmentum is called the mesocortical and mesolimbic projection
-there is better evidence for the mesocortical and mesolimbic pathways being involved in reward
-injections of spiroperidol, a dopamine antagonist, into the nucleus accumbens block the rewarding quality of medial forebrain bundle stimulation, suggesting it as the key site in reward
-further, microinjections of dopamine into the region of the nucleus accumbens are rewarding
-much research attention has focused on the nucleus accumbens as the brain region critical for drugs such as cocaine and amphetamine, which both increase dopamine availability in the synapse

ASCENDING NOCICEPTOR SYSTEMS

- Primary nociceptors are cells with neurites in the periphery, cell bodies in the dorsal root ganglia, and axons inserting into the spinal cord
    -mechanical damage influences the membrane potentials of nociceptors by several means
    -other consequences of tissue damage are the release of histamine and and bradykinin
    -other local messengers include prostaglandin and serotonin, which spread the inflammation and nociceptor discharge to nearby cells, and cause tenderness, or hyperalgesia
    -the volley of nociception is carried centrally by small unmyelinated fibers called C-fibers and by small myelinated fibers called A-delta fibers
    -upon arrival in the cord, the A-delta and C-fibers bifurcate
    -C-fibers terminate in the superficial substantia gelatinosa of the dorsal horn and A-delta fibers terminating superficially as well as deeply
    -pain fibers conduct relatively slowly and project diffusely

Substance P

- Sequence analysis identified Loewi's Substance P as an undecapeptide located heavily in the dorsal horn of the spinal cord
    -peptide is found in tissue section by immunocytochemistry, receptors are found in tissue by autoradiography

-the delay in classifying Substance P as a transmitter is the development of a receptor antagonist

-evidence that Substance P is a transmitter substance comes from studies with capsaicin, which reduced Substance P levels in rats and caused severe losses in nociception

-pain insensitivity syndrome is caused by a depletion of spinal Substance P

The Spinothalamic Tract

- The second-order nociceptors in the cord are of two varieties
  -in superficial layers, there are cells that receive contacts from both A-delta and C-fibers, and only respond to noxious stimuli, called nociceptive specific cells

  -deeper in the dorsal horn are cells that receive projections from mechanoreceptors as well as A-delta receptors, called wide dynamic range cells

  -still deeper in the cord are complex cells, that have loosely organized response properties that may include noxious stimuli in many parts of the body

  -second-order nociceptors cross the midline and ascend to the brainstem in the spinothalamic tract

  -the spinothalamic tract interacts with two thalamic regions, the medial thalamus and the lateral thalamus

  -the medial thalamic projection is thought to organize the affective quality of pain

  -the lateral thalamic projection seems to localize the pain to a particular part of the body

  -thus, pain as commonly experienced invloves the activity of two physiologically and anatomically distinct pathways

Pain and the "Six Principles" of Sensory Physiology

- Adaptation may be exhibited by some pain experiences, but its opposite, summation, also exists
  -action potential frequency codes for stimulus intensity for pure nociceptors, as in other systems

  -however, the magnitude of pain perception is not a direct function of action potential frequency

  -the pain system is poorly organized topographically, compared to other sensory modalities

  -efferent control over the precept also exists with the pain system

DESCENDING ANALGESIA SYSTEMS

- Electrical stimulation of various brainstem sites will render an animal analgesic, or unresponsive to noxious stimuli

-the brainstem structures involved, the periaqueductal gray region and raphe nucleus, influenced pain transmission by a descending pathway called the dorsolateral funiculus

-antagonists to analgesic drugs blocked stimulation-produced analgesia

-finally, it was discovered that endogenous opiate-like molecules existed, and were also blocked by the opiate antagonist naloxone, indicating that they were working at the same receptors as the analgesic drugs

Enkephalins and Endorphins

- The active molecules were found to be peptides of various sizes

  -endorphin, containing 31 amino acids, was the type found primarily in pituitary and brain

  -smaller pentapeptides, the enkephalins, were found in spinal cord and adrenal gland

  -endorphins and enkephalins share sequence homology, and are called opioids, to distinguish them from exogenous opiates

  -the opioids are synthesized as part of large protein precursor molecules and subsequently cleaved into peptides

  -the precursor for endorphin, pro-opiomelanocortin, contains beta-endorphin, as well as ACTH and melanocyte-stimulating hormone

  -pro-enkephalin, the enkephalin precursor, is designed to produce large qualities of opioid exclusively

THE MECHANISM OF OPIOID PEPTIDE ACTION

- Within the spinal cord, enkephalin is especially prevalent in the marginal layers of the dorsal horn, where small diameter nociceptors synapse

  -enkephalins appear to produce analgesia presynaptically, by causing less release of Substance P by first-order nociceptors

The Raphe Nuclei

- Evidence has accumulated that aminergic neurons of the rostroventral medulla (RVM) send fibers down the dorsolateral funiculus to synapse with the enkephalinergic cell

  -serotinergic cells of the nucleus raphe magnus are important in these descending fibers

  -there are also noradrenergic cells of the nucleus subcoeruleus that directly modulate spinal nociception without the medium of the enkephalinergic cell

The Periaqueductal gray

- The raphe nuclei in turn receive a projection from the periaqueductal gray (PAG), which is excitatory to the descending analgesia system
    - the PAG is a region of high opiate receptor density, and microinjections of morphine there will produce analgesia
    - how injections into the PAG cause analgesia when the presumed effect would be inhibition of the descending analgesia circuit, is a dilemma not yet resolved

A Final Common Pathway?

- Beta-endorphin is contained in fibers that terminate in the PAG
    - these fibers originate in the hypothalamic arcuate fasciculus, so that the signal to the PAG may be from the limbic system
    - opioid peptides are also found in other circuits such as basal ganglia
    - it may be these other circuits that produces the euphoria associated with drug use and abuse

Acupuncture

- In 1965, Melzak and Wall produced the gate control theory, postulating that there is a neural pain gate in the spinal cord, that could be open or closed
    - activity of large diameter mechanoreceptors could close the gate when activated
    - Melzak and Wall proposed that some wide dynamic range nociceptors receive an input from an inhibitory interneuron
    - gate control theory has been useful clinically, but the search for the postulated inhibitory circuit has been futile
    - acupuncture and acupressure can alleviate pain even applied far removed from the painful area
    - these procedures probably work by either surround inhibition or a gate control mechanism

Stress-Induced Analgesia

- Stress-induced analgesia is a robust form of analgesia observed in both humans and animals
    - part of stress-induced analgesia is opioid-meidated, but part is not
    - the learned helplessness model is an exciting area of research and a model for stress-induced analgesia
    - candidates for the non-opioid control of analgesia include ACTH and cholecystokinin, but there are numerous other candidate neuromodulators

Lecture Topics:

1. The notion of defining pain and pleasure in animal subjects leads to several interesting topics. If an animal will work for something, can we assume it is pleasurable? Conversely, if they avoid something, can we assume it is painful? How can we ever be sure?

2. If endogenous opioid peptides are released reliably by a given behavior, can a person become addicted to that behavior? Given the current popular press interest in food and sex addictions, might these be real phenomena if they are related to endogenous opioid release?

3. Stress-induced analgesia (SIA) is a robust finding in both humans and animals. Most students will have at least one example from their life of SIA. The purpose of SIA, presumably to inhibit pain to maximze behavioral coping during an emergency, is an interesting topic to discuss.

Overhead Transparencies:

1. Figure 11-2: Self-stimulation Sites in the Brain.

2. Figure 11-11: Descending Analgesia Systems.

3. Figure 11-15: Opioid Receptors in the Spinal Cord.

4. Figure 11-17: Analgesic Intervention in Pain Transmission.

5. Figure 11-19: Gate Control Theory.

Classroom Demonstrations/Student Activities:

1. A hotplate or tailfick device can be used to demonstrate pain thresholds for all the students, and also demostrate the differences in pain thresholds between individuals.

Handouts:

1. Table 11-1: Expressing Pain and Pleasure.

Video List:

<u>Obsessions: The Biological Basis of Addiction.</u> Insight Media. This video discusses addictions, their causes, and some treatment and relief tactics.

CHAPTER 12: HORMONES, SEX, AND REPRODUCTION

Chapter Outline:
HORMONES AND THE "MASTER GLAND"
<u>Peptide Hormones</u>
- Communication between the body and CNS restricted by the hydrophobic blood-brain barrier
    - -hydrophilic compounds cross blood-brain barrier (e.g, adrenaline, thyroxine)

<u>Peptide Synthesis</u>
- All peptides are derived from larger proteins by proteolytic cleavage
    - -insulin: involved in blood glucose regulation
    - -adrenocorticotropic hormone (ACTH): mediates the body's response to stress
- Smaller peptides
    - -neurophysins (e.g., Oxytocin and vasopressin)
    - -hypothalamic releasing factors

<u>The Plan of the Pituitary</u>
- Production of peptide hormones is in the pituitary gland
    - -the portal system
- The posterior lobe
    - -pars nervosa, it is a neural structure
    - -the peptide containing cells are active at different times
    - -vasopressin cells are tonically active, often firing action potentials
    - -oxytocin cells fire phasically
- The anterior lobe
    - -contains both neuroendocrine structures and endocrine cells
    - -contains a larger variety of peptides than posterior lobe
- Homeostasis and negative feedback loops
    - -feedback from endocrine structures result in homeostasis
    - -in negative feedback, the final product acts to inhibit the release of the hormone
    - -hypothalamo-pituitary adrenal axis (HPA axis)-feedback loop incorporating corticotrophin-releasing hormone (CRH), ACTH, and adrenal cortical steroid

THE DETERMINATION OF GENDER
- In mammals (including humans), females have two copies of the X chromosome in each diploid cell while males carry one X and one Y

-Y chromosome contains genetic code for the protein H-Y antigen which works with a testes determination factor to influence the development of the immature gonads into testes and later influences sperm production

Steroid Hormones

- Steroid hormones act by passing directly across the membrane of cells to interact with the target cell to influence the cell's development
- Organizational effects: The cause of physical differences between genders, such as genitalia and musculoskelatal differences, and the nervous system circuits that program reproductive behavior
- Activational effects : Caused by the continued presence of steroid hormones on the organization of structures throughout development that permit the continued expression of sexual physiology

Mechanisms of Steroid Synthesis

- Cholesterol is the biosynthetic precursor for all steroid hormones
    -cholesterol consists of four hydrocarbon rings, a hydroxyl group, and a hydrocarbon chain
- Synthesis of individual hormones
    -progesterone: one of two hormones responsible for female reproduction
    -testosterone: organizational and activational role in male reproduction
    -estradiol: second female reproductive hormone
- Progesterone, testosterone, estradiol, and their intermediaries are found in abundance in blood of both genders
    -it is not the presence of androgen or estrogen (progesterone and estradiol) but the relative quantities that determines gender

Mechanisms of Steroid Action

- Mode of action of non-steroid chemical signals
    -they are hydrophilic, allowing them to diffuse across the extracellular environment to the site of action
- Mode of action of steroids
    -characteristics of steroids: lack charge, are unipolar, and hydrophobic
    -carrier proteins- amphipathic proteins to carry steroids in extracellular space
- Steroid receptor concentrations
    -estrogen: breasts, vagina, uterus, and associated brain regions

-testosterone: genitalia, hair follicles, muscle groups, and associated regions

Primary and Secondary Sexual Characteristics

- Mammalian development initially follows a female program of development
- Primary sexual characteristics
    -on the Y chromosome is a gene for a trophic factor, testes determination factor, which alters the germinal ridge to form a testis instead of an ovary
- Secondary sexual characteristics
    -these are the more visible aspects of an individual's gender.
    -potential to develop into male or female, with a predisposal towards female
    -the internal genitalia initially come in two forms for both genders:
    -1. Wolffian duct is the male system
    -2. Mullerian duct is the female system.

A Critical Period of Development

- Castration of males has feminizing effects
- Feminizing effects of castration were more readily observable when performed early in life (a critical period)

Sexuality in Humans and Other Animals

- Homosexuality as we know it has no natural equivalent in the animal kingdom
    -numerous attempts to explain homosexuality
    -blood Levels of testosterone and sexual behaviors
    -testosterone and male-typed behaviors
    -testosterone increase in male students upon winning
    -correlation between blood testosterone, sexual activity and aging
    -testosterone levels increase from puberty to 20, then drop after age 60
    -Kinsey report (1940) showed sexual activity similar to testosterone levels
    -damage or castration of the testis and physical characteristics

Sexual Dimorphism in the Brain

- Steroids circulate freely in the body and cross the blood-brain barrier
    -a small portion of the cells in the brain have receptors and respond to them, becoming sexually dimorphic nuclei
    -sexual dimorphism in humans is a source of controversy

Steroids and Aggression
- Anabolic steroids
  -little evidence that anabolic steroids enhance athletic performance
- Sex steroids and aggression: the evidence
  -aggressiveness is associated with testosterone only during early development
  -aggressiveness seems to be dependent upon steroid hormones early in life, but less so to a variable degree in adulthood

CONCEPTION, PREGNANCY AND BIRTH
- In mammals, most factors that determine whether sexual behavior will lead to conception is under the control of females
- Receptivity- the female is passive, accepting male sexual activity
- Female selectivity- females are more discriminate, accepting advances only from dominant males
- Proceptivity- the overt seeking of sexual contact by female rats

Regulation of the Estrus and Menstrual Cycles
- Positive and negative feedback loops
  -most systems in the brain are inhibitory: increasing levels of the substance shut down further production of the substance (e.g., the HPA axis)
  -in positive feedback systems, the presence of the substance results in the generation of more of the same substance
  -positive feedback systems include estrus and menstruation.
  -a mechanism in the hypothalamus induces hormone secretion
  -GHRH, and so GH, is released at night
  -GnRH is also released in pulsatile nature, creating higher levels of LH and FSH, and hence sex steroids are dependent upon GnRH levels
- Menstrual cycle
  -the peak of GnRH production in the female with LH initiates ovulation
  -progesterone prepares the uterus for possible pregnancy.
  -inhibin also creates inhibitory loop in the pituitary
- Menstruation and sexual activity
  -estrogen levels seem not to control sexual activity to a great degree in humans.
  -the emergence of civilization with menstrual cycles

Peptide Hormones and Sexual Behavior

- Peptides that regulate reproductive physiology may influence sexual behavior.
    - Lutenizing-hormone Releasing Hormone-(LHRH, also called GnRH) may produce sexual behavior in female mammals.
    - Oxytocin and vasopressin may influence sexual behavior in males, and may generate maternal behaviors in females.
- Mechanisms of peptide action
    - peptide may get into the brain to activate receptors

Endocrine control of Pregnancy and Parturition

- Prenatal levels: progesterone remains high through pregnancy, steadily rising in humans. Estradiol levels start low and steadily increase.
- Perinatal level: progesterone levels drop but estradiol levels remain high. In mother, oxytocin surges briefly after birth to expel the placenta and contracts the uterus to control bleeding. Prolactin levels increase to increase milk production.

PHEROMONES

- A type of chemical signal with sexually attracting or repulsing effects, or communicating information about sexual condition.
    - different organisms rely on different pheromones
- Roles of Pheromones in Rodents in Determining Estrus
    - Lee-Boot Effect- in the absence of male cues, estrus among females ceases.
    - Whitten Effect- females synchronize their estrus cycles
    - Bruce Effect- the presence of an unknown male terminates a pregnancy.
    - Vandenbergh Effect- the presence of males accelerates puberty in female mice.
    Pheromones in Humans
    - Human equivalents of the Whitten effect have been shown

NEURAL CIRCUITS FOR MATING AND REPRODUCTION

- Mating consists of discrete stages, or fixed action patterns
    - 1. Copulation (proximate fixed action patterns)
    - 2. Attraction and arousal (ultimate fixed action patterns)

Spinal and Brainstem Circuits

- Females: lordosis- The fixed action pattern of adopting a position allowing for male intromission.
- Males: proximate fixed action patterns include erection, intromission, and ejaculation.
- Sexual dimorphism: dimorphism in genitalia creates dimorphism among motor neurons controlling their muscles.

Forebrain Circuits

- In mammals
  - medial amygdaloid nucleus (AME)
  - a steroid concentrating, sexually dimorphic nucleus of the limbic system that instigates proximal stages of sexual behavior.
  - limbic vasopressin, oxytocin, or other peptides produces ultimate aspects of sexual behavior.
- Sexual attraction in females
  - ultimate features of female sexual behavior are as recognizable as the male's behaviors involving similar limbic structures.

Lecture Topics:

1.   At several points in the chapter humans are distinguished from other organisms (even primates).   Students can debate whether humans are in fact separate from other, even closely related organisms in this way.   What roles do civilization and consciousness play in this debate? Revisit the mind-body problem. Can we transcend our physiological drives?

2.   Because it is of central importance to reproduction strategies in organisms, the role of evolution should be highlighted throughout discussion of this chapter.   What evolutionary arguments may be made to support the extensive roles of physiological elements in reproduction?   What role may cultural evolution play in these discussions?

3.   Because of the underlying physiological nature of much sexual activity, there are many proposed means of controlling sexual behavior through chemical interventions.   The chapter points to many examples of attempts to control negative behavior in this way, yet neglects the potential positive contributions.   For example, what therapies may be used to promote pregnancy or increase otherwise low sex drives?

4.   A distinction may be made between biological gender and gender-typed behaviors.   A biological female may act more consistently as a typical male, and vice versa.   This suggest that behavior does not necessarily derive naturally from underlying biology, but is shaped by many factors.   The class may discuss what other factors may be involved.   Keeping in mind that there is an underlying biological difference between the sexes, what weight should this be given relative to the role of the other factors the group identifies?

Overhead Transparencies:

1. Figure 12-5: The HPA Axis.

2. Figure 12-7: Embryonic Development of Gonads.

3. Figure 12-9: Steroid Action.

4. Figure 12-10: Male Testosterone Levels and Age, Frequency of Male Sexual Episodes and Age.

5. Figure 12-15: Female Periovulatory Sexual Interest.

Classroom Demonstrations/Student Activities:

1. Homosexuality in humans is possibly unique in the animal world. Groups of students may investigate this possibility as part of the debate about the origins of homosexuality. There is no shortage of theories about the origins of homosexuality. Students can identify one, explore the empirical basis for the theory, and have an open debate in class.

2. To demonstrate the relation between the menstrual cycle and sexual interest in females, female students (with anonymity) can record their menstrual cycle and each day of the cycle rate their sex drive. This should be done at several points in the day for each month of the semester. This can then be contrasted with the relatively independent cycles of male sexual interest. The men can also are their interest in sex using the same approximate schedule as the women in class.

3. If a colony of animals is available, several of the rat studies presented in the chapter may be replicated. For example, the cycles of estrus for females caged with only other females, with only other males, with a mixed group, and with only a single male.

Handouts:

Several figures or tables in the text could be distributed for frequent reference by the class:

1. Figure 12-7: Embryonic Development of Gonads.

2. Table 12-1: Steroid Levels in the Blood.

3. Figure 12-14: Events of the Human Menstrual Cycle.

Video List:

1. The classic PBS video The Miracle of Life from 1980 provides stunning footage of early prenatal development including discussions of chemical actions prior to, during, and after pregnancy.

2. Desmond Morris's The Human Animal series presents evolutionary perspectives on the development of human relationships, including sexual relationships. He discusses the biological basis of the pair-bond. This is a graphic video that also includes discussions about changes in sperm count due to partner separation and the evolutionary advantage of female infidelity.

3. The PBS series The Mind episode 3: Aging has a brief segment on the relation between stress and health, with a focus on the role of cortisol and stress in preventing illness.

4. The PBS series The Brain has an episode (#6: The Two Brains) with segments about hormones and sexual development, the social influences on sexual development, and episode 3, Rhythms and Drives discusses aggression and the brain, with brief discussion of the role of testosterone.

5. Sexuality and Aging available from Fanlight Productions is a detailed examination of changes in sexuality and intimacy into late adulthood. Though primarily examining social changes which occur, there is discussion of physiological changes which impact intimacy and sexuality.

6. The Gay Gene, available from Films for the Humanities and Sciences, examines the quest for explanations of homosexuality, with emphasis on genetic theories. This film compliments the extent, which is more highly critical than the film presentation.

7. Multiple Genders: Mind and Body available from Films for the Humanities and Sciences, looks at the complexities in defining gender based upon the experience of transsexuals and hermaphrodites. This is an especially interesting film because it combines scientific, philosophical, and theological perspectives on sexuality.

8. Men, Women, and the Sex Difference: Boys and Girls are Different is an ABC special report examining the social and physiological factors that impact development of gender identity. It presents brain differences between genders while at the same time discussing the role of different experiences in showing gender during life.

CHAPTER 13: SLEEP AND DREAMING

Chapter Outline:

CIRCADIAN RHYTHMS

- Circadian rhythm refers to an "endogenous daily cycle that controls...various behavioral and physiological changes in plants and animals" (p. 305)
  -sleep/wake is one example
  -in humans sleep/wake is 25 hours
  -most circadian rhythms are 24-hours
  -factors Influencing Cycle (*zeitgeber*)
  -primary zeitgeber in human sleep/wake is the sun

Where is the clock?

- Site for generating endogenous rhythms is the suprachiasmatic nucleus (SCN)
  -lesions to SCN result in disruption of sleep-wake cycle
  -light is the primary zeitgeber, so the SCN must receive input from the retinas, the retinohypothalamic tract
  -transmitters Involved: AVP, GABA, $GABA_A$ and $GABA_B$ receptors
- Seasonal rhythms
  -rhythms such as those controlling hibernation and mating
  -control seems to be located in the pineal gland and due to melatonin

STAGES OF SLEEP

- Sleep differs from unconsciousness because there are distinct stages of sleep
  -electrical activity in the brain not change significantly as we sleep
  -the endogenous sleep cycle is 25 hours long
  -two distinct divisions of sleep. each exhibiting its own physiological and behavioral characteristics
  -non-REM (NREM) Sleep and REM sleep alternate in 90 minute cycles

The EEG and EMG

- The electroencephalogram (records electrical activity in the brain)
  -the frequency (cycles per second) and amplitude (size) of the electrical potentials are recorded
  -based upon frequency and amplitude, sleep divided into four stages:

1. Alpha: (8-13 Hz), 10-20 µV
2. Beta: (13-30 Hz), up to 30 µV
3. Theta: (4-7 Hz), up to 50µV
4. Delta: (0.5-4 Hz), up to 100 µV

- The electromyogram (records electrical potentials of muscles)
  -EMG activity is highest during wakefulness, and decreases through sleep until it is nonexistent in REM sleep

Non-REM (NREM) Sleep

- Sometimes referred to as quiet sleep, characterized by low frequency, synchronous brain activity and relaxed muscle tone
- Stage 1 (1-7 minutes, and accounts for 4-5% of sleep time)
  -after a brief period of drowsiness, the alpha pattern is replaced by theta waves
  -person is easily woken so this is called low arousal threshold
- Stage 2 (lasts for 10-25 minutes, comprising 45-55% of sleep time)
  -Sleep spindles- A burst of 11 to 15 Hz waves lasting for 0.5 to 1.5 seconds
  -K complexes- high voltage waves that have a sharp negative component followed by a slower positive wave
- Stage 3 (4-6% of sleep time, is a blend of theta and delta waves)
- Stage 4 (comprises 12-15% of sleep time)
  -deepest sleep, combined with stage 3 is called slow wave sleep
  -primarily delta activity
  -sleep terrors- episodes in which the person awakes suddenly in terror
  -somnambulism- sleep walking
  -stages 3 and 4 show a decrease in sympathetic nervous system activity and an increase in parasympathetic activity

Rapid Eye Movement (REM) Sleep

- Characterized by desynchronized (low-voltage/mixed frequency) waves, muscle atonia, period bursts of rapid eye movements
  -despite muscle flacidity, brain activity closely resembles awake state
  -EEG may contain sawtooth waves.
  -in mammals, ponto-geniculoccipital (PGO) spike, generated by the pons
  -muscle atonia due to inhibitory hyperpolarization of alpha motor neuron
  -not complete- diaphragm, heart, and eye muscles are active

-sexual arousal evident for both males and females, regardless of dream content
-rapid eye movements unrelated to dream content

NEURAL MECHANISMS FOR SLEEP AND WAKING
- No simple system that maintains the sleep/wake cycle.
    -during wakefulness there is an accumulation of sleep-inducing substances and during sleep there is an accumulation of wake-inducing substances

The Search for the "Sleep Transmitter"
- Serotonin
    -administering a serotonin precursor (5-HTP) enhances slow wave sleep
- Sleep Peptides
    -factor S: enhances slow wave sleep and increases body temperature
    -delta sleep-inducing peptide (DSIP): increases delta sleep activity
    -adenosine (inhibits of transmitters associated with arousal, eg., NE and ACh)

Transmitter Systems and "Arousal"
- Arousal system is thought to produce both waking in the sleep/wake cycle, as well as increased awareness during waking.
    -primary substances involved are transmitters
- Acetylcholine
    -regulates circadian rhythms through interaction with the SCN
    -acetylcholine appears to regulate muscle atonia during REM sleep
- Norepinephrine
    -locus coeruleus: the primary site of NE regulation of wakefulness and REM
    -NE is used in several transmitter systems with distinct receptor populations; neurotransmitter effects are a function of the receptor, not the transmitter
    -dopamine concentrations are high during waking and decrease during sleep
- Histamine
    -two receptors, H_1 and H_2
    -histamine levels fluctuate with circadian rhythms
    -histamine influences alertness during waking portion of sleep/wake cycle

<u>Neural Mechanisms of Dreaming</u>
- Most dreams occur during REM
- Activation-synthesis Theory of Dreaming
    -dreaming is due to an activation of forebrain cognitive structures which are also active during the day but not active during nonREM sleep combing memories with signals generated by the brain
    -REM sleep and dreaming suppressed by tricyclic antidepressants and serotonin

WHY DO WE SLEEP?
<u>Sleep in Evolutionary Perspective</u>
- Sleep occurs in all vertebrates, only warmblooded animals experience REM sleep.
- Immobilization theory (Webb)
    -sleep is adaptive because it keeps animals out of danger.
- Energy conservation theory
    -inactivity during periods following food gathering conserves energy
    -sleep time and metabolic activity have a common ontogenic pattern
    -sleep patterns do differ across species
<u>Restoration or Elimination?</u>
- Restorative theory
    -period of rest allows metabolism and protein synthesis.
    -about 80% of the secretion of growth hormone occurs during sleep
    -nonREM important for body restoration, REM important for brain restoration
- Elimination theory
    -sleep may rid the body of waste material or excessive sensory input
    -REM sleep allows for reverse learning of inappropriate behavioral patterns
<u>Jouvet's Theory of Sleep</u>
- Genetic Programming Hypothesis
    -REM sleep needed to modify existing behavior patterns by facilitating transcription of genetic material
    -REM deprivation leads to an inability to alter innate patterns resulting in stereotypic behavior
<u>Psychological Theories of Sleep</u>
- Sigmund Freud

-distinguished between the manifest content, the actual dream, and the latent content, the underlying psychological associations
- Carl Jung
    -dreams express themes from the collective unconscious (instincts from the primitive components of the mind)
- Problem-solving theories
    -sleep may be needed to consolidate complex learning for such things as faces and conversations

SLEEP DISORDERS
Insomnias
- General symptomology
    -misinterpretation of symptoms has led to changing the classification of insomnia as a disorder to a symptom
    -35% of adults experience some insomnia, half reporting serious problems
    -primary complaints are of difficulty in falling asleep, frequent awakenings, short sleep time, and unrefreshing sleep
    -many people report daytime symptoms, including fatigue, irritability, depression, anxiety, mood changes, and inability to concentrate
- Classified into types based upon underlying causes:
    -behavioral or psychophysiological
    -psychiatric disorders
    -neurological disorders
    -environmental causes
    -treatments vary based upon the causes though most do not seek treatment

Disorders of Rhythmically
- Seasonal Affective Disorder (SAD)
    -onset of depression typically, mid- to late fall through winter
    -major treatment is light therapy: exposure to 2,000 lux for two or more hours
    -delayed sleep phase syndrome: very late sleep onset and a late arousal time
    -treatment is by chronotherapy : bedtime is delayed by increasing increments
    -jet lag: results from rapid travel across time zones
    -symptoms: fatigue, insomnia, and gastrointestinal problems

-shift-work disorder: disorder affecting persons who work unusual hours
-symptoms: disturbed sleep patterns, fatigue, gastritis, and ulcers

<u>Other Disorders</u>

- Narcolepsy
    -sleep attacks which occur uncontrollably and at inappropriate times
    -caused by an activation of the neural mechanisms causing REM sleep.
    -REM Sleep Behavior Disorder: REM sleep without muscle atonia
- Sleep Apnea
    -central sleep apnea syndrome
    -a loss of respiratory effort, resulting in cessation of air flow
    -obstructive sleep apnea syndrome
    -due to an upper airway obstruction, including narrow nasal airway, enlarged tonsils, tongue tissues, or an enlarged soft palate
- Sudden Infant Death Syndrome (SIDS)
    -there are a number of predisposing factors: low birthweight, premature birth, maternal smoking during pregnancy, twins or multiple births, and hereditary factors
- Drug Dependency Insomnia
    -results from long-term use of barbiturate or benzadiazepine sleep medications.

Lecture Topics:

1. There are a number of different substances which play complex roles in the regulation of sleep and waking. Lecture can revisit these by generating a list as well as the evidence to support the role(s) played by each substance. This underscores the scientific methods used, as well as the dictum that receptor sites, not transmitters, determine action.

2. There are a number of theories of sleep, each more or less addressing how sleep evolved (that is, what is its purpose?). The text presents some of the basic ideas about using evolution to explain sleep. Students may generate their own "evolutionary theory" or they may confront the larger teleological issue, does sleep have to serve any purpose?

3. The nature of dreams is partly important because people's implicit theories of dreams impact how they respond to dreams that they have had. For example, a student dreams he or she has failed a major exam, and then the person wakes up and must go confront the test. One way to showcase different theories of dreams is to have a student report on a dream he or she had. Others can then "interpret" the dream using each of the theories of dreams as a guide.

4. Part of the complexity of understanding sudden infant death syndrome is that it so closely resembles sleep apnea that cases may not be properly identified. In recent years news reports have been rife with stories about parents killing their children then blaming the deaths on SIDS. In some cases this seems to have occurred within the same family affecting multiple children. Thus, the parents may repeatedly kill their infants, blaming SIDS for each successive case. While this behavior is obviously reprehensible, it creates important challenges for the medical and legal community in identifying accurately cases of SIDS. These challenges may lead to spirited debate.

Overhead Transparencies:

1. Figure 13-4: Cycles of Sleep.

2. Figure 13-5: EEG Patterns.

3. Figure 13-6: Stages of Sleep.

4. Figure 13-10: Development and Treatment of Insomnia.

Classroom Demonstrations/Student Activities:

1. Students may create a sleep log, tracking their own sleep habits (time to sleep, time awake, if waking was naturally occurring or other (alarm-clock) induced, and any dreams that they recall. After a 2-3 week period of this log students can see the regularities in their own habits, or identify factors which mat contribute to irregularity of habits.

2. Students can do their own "dream analysis" by writing down the content of their dreams. These records may be passed around a classroom (be sure no names are used) and others can interpret the dreams as well. Afterwards, students can discuss what factors may have influenced how they interpreted the dreams of others.

3. Students may try to experience the problem-solving during sleep hypothesized by Schatzman. Pass out a sealed envelope with a complex word problem written on it. Tell students to open the envelope and read the problem before going to sleep. Impress upon them that they should not attempt to solve the problem, but simply be sure it is on their mind before falling asleep. Ask them to write out the solutions in the morning, after they have "slept on it." A further demonstration would be to ask them to solve a similar, but different, problem at the start or class. How many arrive at the answer?

Handouts:

1. Figure 13-5: EEG Patterns is a good reference for students to have.

2. A handout may be prepared similar to Table 13-1, but include research support (See Lecture Topic #1, above).

Video List:

1. One episode in the PBS series "The Brain" concerns sleep (Episode #3: Rhythms and Drives) and another concerns dreaming (Episode #8: States of Mind). Both of these episodes have general information, but episode #3 has an excellent segment on changing work schedules.

2. The Story of Carl Gustov Jung is a 3 video series which follows Jung's life and theory as they develop. It is especially worthwhile because of archival footage of Jung discussing his theory, in particular dreams (Episode 2: 67,000 Dreams).

3. Sleep Disorders....Their Effects and Treatments is available through Insight Media. This is both informative in content, as well as therapeutic in that sleep experts talk about avoiding sleep disorders.

4. Rhythm and Blues, available through Insight Media, focuses on the biological effects of changing sleep/wake patterns for work or other reasons. It focuses especially on recent attempts to provide relief for those who must confront such changes in patterns (e.g., pilots, firemen).

5. The Royal Road: Psychoanalytic Approaches to the Dream from Insight Media is an intense case study of a single dream and the process used by a psychotherapist to uncover the meaning within the dream.

CHAPTER 14: EATING, DRINKING, AND HOMEOSTASIS

Chapter Outline:

BRAIN METABOLISM
- Brain is the most metabolically active organ in the body
- Homeostasis is dependent upon meeting the brain's needs

Blood-Brain Barrier and Glucose Utilization
- Blood-brain barrier (BBB)
  - tight junctions: formed at all interfaces between blood and brain when a cell's surface closely contacts adjacent cells, leaving no space between the two
  - selective carriers and ion pumps are located on the interface cells
  - glucose crosses by a pump governed by a constant, Michaelis constant (K_m)
- Metabolism of glucose
  - glucose metabolized to produce energy or converted to amino acids and lipids
  - glucose goes first through glycolysis (See Chapter 2), is converted to pyruvic acid and goes through the Krebs Cycle
  - metabolism in the absence of glucose

Oxygen Requirements
- Brain of an average sized person consumes 49 ml/min of oxygen
  - the entire body of an average person consumes only 250 ml/min, thus the brain, accounting for 2% of body weight uses 20% of the oxygen
  - in children, the brain uses as much as 50% of the oxygen consumed

Circulation Requirements
- The brain accounts for about 15% of all cardiac output
  - blood flow in the brain must be constant and within narrow parameters

Glucose Requirements
- 25% of blood glucose is used by the brain

BLOOD FLOW
Perfusion Pressure and Autoregulation
- Perfusion Pressure is equal to the difference between the arterial blood pressure and the cerebral venous pressure
- Autoregulation

-the process by which cerebral vessels alter their diameter to maintain a constant blood flow despite changes in perfusion pressure
-1.   metabolic hypothesis: explains vasodilation (widening) is response to hypotension (low blood pressure)
-2.   myogenic hypothesis: accounts for vasoconstriction in response to increased blood pressure
-3.   neurogenic hypothesis: changes in vessel diameter are under sympathetic or parasympathetic control
-sources of input: venous pressure, CSF pressure, and carbon dioxide levels
-neurotransmitters may effect cerebral blood flow directly (e.g., peptides) or indirectly (e.g., norepinephrine, dopamine, serotonin, and GABA).

Blood Supply and Anoxia
- Internal cartoid arteries merge with the basilar artery (a junction of two vertebral arteries), giving rise to the Circle of Willis
    -anoxia: No blood oxygen
    -asphyxia: Low blood carbon dioxide

ENERGY USE
- High energy required for transmitter synthesis, packaging, secretion, uptake, and sequestration; ion pumping to maintain ionic gradients; intracellular transport; synthesis of lipids and complex macromolecules

Cooling Mechanisms
- Human brain cannot tolerate large increases in temperature
    -in all mammals, cool arterial blood serves to dissipate heat
    -carnivores and hooved animal cooling systems: blood cooled through evaporation in the muzzle is passed through the rete mirabile, a tangle of small arteries in the cavernous sinus, cooling the brain
    -human brain cooling: blood can return through the external jugular vein or an internal pathway

TECHNIQUES FOR STUDYING BRAIN ACTIVITY
- Correlate spontaneous or experimentally induced alterations in the composition of blood, CSF, or both, with changes in cerebral physiological functions or CSF mediated behavior
    -radioactive tracers: used to study specific glucose metabolites

-administering radioactive precursors then later removing the
-brain and evaluating the by-products of the precursor

EATING
Homeostasis
- Maintenance of stable internal environment, including water, heat, oxygen, and energy reserves
    -set point: optimal level of activity
    -body weight and metabolism (Brownell, et al., 1986)
    -dieting rats lost weight half as fast as controls, but regained it three times as fast as controls
    -to have adequate glucose, food must be ingested and glucose released for use
    -absorption phase: food enters the digestive tract and level of glucose in blood increases; excess glucose is stored as body fat, glycogen, and proteins
    -fasting phase: energy is extracted from fat and glycogen stores
    -during the fasting phase the brain gets energy from glycogen while other cells get energy elsewhere

Role of Glucose in Eating Behavior
- Glucostatic theory: level of blood glucose controls eating behavior
- Role of the lateral hypothalamus
    -cells in the liver monitor glucose levels and communicate to the brain
    -lateral hypothalamus contains receptors able to measure glucose directly

Role of Lipids in Eating Behavior
- During absorption, glucose is converted to fat
- Lipostatic theory: eating is controlled by mechanisms designed to achieve a set point for weight

Hypothalamic Circuits
- Lesions to lateral hypothalamus (LH): result in enhanced breakdown of fat stores by the release of glucagon from the pancreas, and stimulates the digestion of triglycerides in fat tissue, increasing free fatty acids in the blood
    -lesions to ventromedial Hypothalamus (VMH): result in dramatic weight change
    -brown adipose tissue cells are stimulated by the hypothalamus to become active after feeding, producing a rise in temperature

<u>Role of Monoamines and Peptide Hormones in Feeding</u>
- Norepinephrine inhibits activity of satiety-producing cells
  - -serotonin is released from LH following food ingestion dopamine in LH suppresses food intake
  - -neuropeptide Y (NPY) induces physiological changes that increase appetite
  - -dynorphin (an endorphin) increases tendency to eat
  - -hypothalamic growth hormone-releasing factor stimulates food intake

EATING DISORDERS
<u>Obesity</u>
- In U.S., 30% of adults are significantly over weight, 12% being grossly so.
  - -high levels of insulin promotes buildup of fat
- Homeostatic causes
  - -decreased sensitivity in VMH or hyperresponsivity following LH input results in weight gain
  - -weight cycling leads to more rapid weight gain and slower weight loss
  - -opioid peptides have been found in genetically obese rats, and stimulate food intake when injected into VMH of sated rats

<u>Anorexia Nervosa</u>
- 1 to 2% of population, most common in teenage girls (1 in 10 cases is male)
  - -symptomology: severe self-starvation accompanied by psychological disturbances, dramatic weight loss (25% of body weight), self induced emesis (vomiting), excessive exercise, or abuse of laxatives, intense fear of becoming fat and a distortion of body image, amenorrhea (cessation of menstruation) or loss of sexual potency for males
  - -10% never recover and die due to complications
  - -disturbances in sexual function, water regulation, and temperature implicate the hypothalamus as a potential biological source of anorexia
  - -response to antidepressants suggest a link between depression and anorexia
  - -norepinephrine injected into the hypothalamus of animals stimulates the animals to eat
  - -conditioned food aversion

<u>Bulimia</u>
- 1-5% of young women in America.

-symptoms: recurrent compulsive eating (binge eating) of massive quantities of food in short time, a fearful preoccupation with getting fat, and behaviors aimed at counteracting the fattening effects of food, such as induced vomiting or laxative abuse

-bulimics tend to maintain their body weight

- Causes

-monoamines such as serotonin, gonadotropins, thyroid hormones, and norepinephrine seem to be influenced in bulimics as they are in anorexics

- Treatments

-antidepressants, including naltrexone leading to decreases in binging and purging behaviors

DRINKING

- Upon drinking a signal is sent to the brain that the thirst has been satisfied

-water absorption then occurs, taking 10-40 minutes

-water is a more basic need than is food

-ion concentrations must be kept constant (within 2%) for all cells to function

Thirst

- osmotic thirst: ion concentration is higher in the extracellular environment than in the cell, causes water to diffuse into the extracellular space from inside the cell
- volemic thirst: is a water deficit in the extracellular environment as it idffuses into the cell

-osmoreceptors: biological devices specializing in detecting osmolarity that become active when they shrink through their own dehydration

-baroreceptors: volume receptors in the atria of the heart and kidneys are sensitive to pressure changes in the blood

Kidney

- Structure (See Figure 14-15)

-the nephron made of a bulb (Bowman's capsule) and the glomerulus

-blood enters the kidney through the renal artery directly from the aorta; the artery branches into arterioles which each penetrate a Bowman's capsule

-the kidney removes salt and water from blood then restores the amount needed by the blood to maintain proper tonicity

Hormonal Modulation: Aldosterone, Vasopressin, and Angiotensin

- Aldosterone is a steroid hormone that causes kidneys to retain water
- Vasopressin causes kidneys to conserve water before we feel thirsty
    - volemic thirst and the renin-angiotensin cascade
    - when water and salt stores are depleted, kidney secretes an enzyme, renin, converted into angiotensin
    - stimulates the release of aldosterone to conserves sodium in the kidney
    - stimulates release of vasopressin to conserves water in the kidney
    - the subfornical organ (SFO) regulates thirst
    - restoration of osmolarity is not simultaneous with drinking
    - we respond to the presence of water, not homeostasis

Lecture Topics:

1.   The behaviors of binging and purging seen in bulimia present several problems which are presented in the text to be reiterated in lecture.   Students should consider not only these, but also the ramifications for the bulimic taken from the Brownell, et al. (1896) study involving obese cycling rats.   The binge-purge cycle is not unlike the protocol for these rats.   How will this help to perpetuate the bulimic behaviors?   Can students generate ideas about how to break the cycle?

2.   Homeostasis provides yet another opportunity to address the mind-body problem.   For example, there is clear evidence that hunger is regulated by biological processes.   It is also, clear, however, that eating disorders result in large part from social and psychological factors around the individual.   Among the implications of this is that there are two kinds of eating behavior: physiologically necessitated, and emotionally necessitated.   What are the implications of such a dichotomy?   How would we use this knowledge to develop interventions for those with eating disorders?

3.   The renin-angiotensin cascade is a complex system which regulates drinking behavior.   By contrast, the systems which regulate eating are more direct and simplistic.   How could these two systems have evolved?   Why would the drinking system be so much more complex?   Could this be due to the aquatic origins of life?

4.   The blood-brain barrier provides a formidable obstacle to any substance trying to impact the cells of the brain.   Why do you suppose such a barrier exists?   Clearly, it would be easier for nutrients to reach the brain if they did not need to be actively transported across the barrier.   The only other analog to the BBB occurs during pregnancy at the umbilical cord.   Reasons for this can be discussed and evolutionary advantages considered.

Overhead Transparencies:

1.   Figure 14-2: Metabolism of Glucose in the Brain.

2.   Table 14-2: Effect of Neurotransmitters on the Cerebral Circulation.

3.   Figure 14-14: Thirst.

4. Figure 14-16: Summary of the Renin-Angiotensin Cascade.

Classroom Demonstrations/Student Activities:

1. Students can chart their eating habits and feelings of hunger. Have students chart when and what they eat, then, ask them to record at five minute intervals on a scale of 1-5 (5=very hungry) their hunger. Students can examine their average number of trials until they score a "5" in relation to others, as well as in relation to the type of food they consumed.

2. Bulimia is often considered to be a disorder occurring on a continuum. Several researchers argue that most people exhibit binge and purge behaviors at times. To illustrate this, ask students to record their eating, drinking, and exercise habits for several days (2 weeks works best). This should be done BEFORE eating disorders are discussed, and students should have their data available when the topic is discussed.
Without compromising privacy, ask students to consider if they alter their behaviors (eating or exercise) in response to immediately preceding behaviors. For example, you can ask students to consider how many meals they skip after a meal during which the "pigged out" or how many exercised only after long periods of eating.

Handouts:

1. Figure 14-9, the Structure of the Hypothalamus is an essential diagram for student to have in order to understand what portions of this region are involved in hunger.

2. Figure 14-15, the Structure of the Kidney will greatly aid in explaining how the kidney performs its function.

3. Figure 14-18, the Communication Between the Kidney and the Brain illustrates this complex system and should be a useful reference.

Video List:

1. The Endocrine System, available through Insight Media, examines the mechanisms by which hormones regulate bodily functions. While it focuses primarily on hormonal activity, there is brief discussion

the systems by which these hormones trigger hunger and thirst. Excellent animations and photographs enhance this video.

2. Endocrine control: Systems in balance, also available through insight media focuses specifically on maintenance of homeostasis and the mechanisms which work to maintain it.

3. Eating disorders: When food hurts from Hacienda Productions is a documentary designed for training paraprofessionals to recognize the issues involved in eating disorders. It is low on biology, but high on presenting the turmoil persons with eating disorders confront.

4. Eating disorders from Dartmouth-Hitchcock Medical Center traces the development of eating disorders and their symptoms. This brief (half hour) video is an intense experience. Like #3 above, however, it is not very high on the biology, but there are some examples in the video.

CHAPTER 15: DEVELOPMENT AND LEARNING

Chapter Outline:
DEVELOPMENT OF THE NERVOUS SYSTEM
- Neuronal plasticity: ability of the nervous system to reorganize and regenerate

NEUROGENESIS
<u>Embryonic Development and Induction</u>
- Formation of the blastocyst
    -gastrulation and neurolation
<u>Cell Proliferation</u>
- The Process of cell proliferation: neural mitosis
    -cell migration following proliferation

NEURONAL MIGRATION
- Neuroblast - precursor neuronal cell which has yet to have a location, transmitter and shape- extends part of the cell body in one direction then pulling

NEURONAL DIFFERENTIATION
- Neighbor interactions, environmental molecular cues, and surrounding electrical activity influence cell maturation and differentiation
<u>Neuronal Fate Determination</u>
- Determined by genetic information, environmental factors, and cell to cell interactions
<u>Determination of Neurotransmitter Phenotype</u>
- Neurotransmitter phenotype is dependent upon environmental cues
    -sympathetic neurons in ANS all originate with noradrenergic properties but some change to cholinergic (using acetylcholine)
    -Schotzinger and Landis showed that the transmitter is flexible and may be changed very late in development
<u>Development of Electrical Properties</u>
- Electrical properties change during development
    -in amphibian spinal cells, excitability is characterized by a change from Ca^{++} dependent action to a brief Na^+ impulse
    -calcium channel activity associated with neurotransmitter release in adults directs cerebellar cells before contacts are established

AXON DEVELOPMENT AND GROWTH CONE GUIDANCE

- Neuron develops a dendritic arbor to support input to the cell
  - neuron must also extend its axon to find its target cells (growth cone)

Tropic Factors and Other Guides

- Tropic factors provide directional cues for axons, through attraction, adhesions, or repulsion
  - central nervous system and peripheral nervous system growth cones collapse and retract when they come into contact

Adhesion Molecules

- Three families categorized by structure:
  - neural cell adhesion molecule (NCAM), cadherin (e.g., N-cadherin), and integrins

Molecular Gradients

- Regions were molecules are more concentrated at one end than an other
  - growing neurons follow gradients to find a location within a region

SYNAPTOGENESIS

- Pre- and post-synaptic membranes and specializations must form in order to maintain the synapse, if no contact is made, neuron sending the axon may die
  - motor neuron growth cone extends to muscle target, releasing small amounts of acetylcholine (ACh) and developing muscle cells respond
  - basal lamina is the extracellular matrix containing molecules needed for the formation and maintenance of synapses

ACTIVITY-DEPENDENT FINE-TUNING OF THE NERVOUS SYSTEM

- More neurons and axons are generated during development than are needed
  - extras are eliminated through "competitive interaction."
  - activity-dependent segregation in visual cortex models synaptic modification

LEARNING THEORY

- Learning: process by which experience alters behavior, presumably through changing the nervous system through neural plasticity
  - several types of learning:
  - complex learning: forms of learning not easily classified

-reflexive learning- simple forms of learning which may occur in peripheral rather than central nervous system, may be due to changes in synaptic efficiency
-nonassociative and simple associative learning- simple forms of learning that may be observed in vertebrates and invertebrates
-changes in physiological, morphological, or biochemical make-up result in changes in behavior

Nonassociative Learning: Habituation and Sensitization

- Habituation: a progressively weaker response to a repeated stimulus over time
- Sensitization: an increased response to a repeated weak stimulus following arousal due to a noxious or intense stimulus..

Associative Learning

- Involves "making a connection" between events or stimuli
  -classical conditioning: development of an association between a relevant unconditional stimulus (US) which leads to an unconditioned response (CR), and a conditioned stimulus (CS) that does not initially produce the behavior
  -operant conditioning: association between a behavior and an event or consequence in the environment
  -food aversion: special model of classical and operant conditioning, requires only one occurrence to change behavior

Complex Learning

- Includes many types of learning, from plasticity to instinctive behavior to higher cognitive functions
  -imprinting: classical conditioning of a strong attachment between an animal and the first stimulus it encounters after birth
  -observational learning: includes skill and language acquisition in humans
  -latent learning: "learning" nonspecific information about an environment which later facilitates specific learning within that environment
  -spatial learning: used to navigate through the environment

SIMPLE SYSTEM MODELS FOR PLASTICITY

- Although gross-level changes may be observed in complex, freely behaving organisms, such information does not show cellular changes

The Virtue of Simple Systems

- Invertebrates have fewer neurons (and connections) than vertebrates
    - in some animals these neurons are large enough to see under weak magnification, are in the same location for all individuals, and are easily accessible for study in behaving organisms

Aplysia and *Hermissenda*

- Gill-withdrawal reflex in *Aplysia*
    - stimulus contacting the mantle or siphon causes the gill to retract
    - electrophysiological activity can be measured at the sensory (presynaptic) and motor (postsynaptic) neurons during the learning of the response reveals that change occurs at the synapse between the pre- and postsynaptic cells
    - *Hermissenda* has two types of photoreceptors that are mutually inhibitory:
    - type A cells leads to positive phototaxis, type B cells inhibit type A
    - with conditioning, type B cell K^+ currents are prolonged, increasing their response, more strongly inhibiting type A cells

Other Simple Systems

- Although the nervous system of *Drosophila melanogaster* is inaccessible, we can link specific deficits with specific genetic mutations

VERTEBRATE MODELS FOR PLASTICITY

- Several criteria must be met to establish biological explanation for learning:
    - loss of function when brain area is removed
    - electrophysiological activity in that region must correspond to learning
    - time of change must correspond with learning
    - inhibition of identified processes must result in loss of function

The Search for the Engram

- Lashley studied maze learning in rats, and the effects of either knife cuts or ablations to cerebral cortex on this learning
    - the area of damage was less important that the amount of cortex damaged

Hebb's Postulate

- Hebb (a student of Lashley) believed specific neural changes underlie learning
    - -a synapses is strengthened by activity between pre- and postsynaptic cells
    - -Memories stored in networks of neurons called cell assembly, connected by synapses strengthened by concurrent activation

Enriched Environments
- Hebb concluded that the enriched environment experienced by rats (being played with by his children then returned to the lab) lead to an increase in the rat's learning ability

Discrete Stages of Learning (See Figure 15-19)
- Hebb's Dual Trace Theory of Memory
    - -short-term memory lasts for minutes to hours, establishment of a neural circuit that encodes through concurrent activity
    - -long-term memory lasts days to months
    - -consolidation leads to enduring cellular change
    - -acquisition is the period of actual learning
    - -retrieval of stored information

The Functional Organization of Memory
- Milner studied the effects of temporal lobe removal on memory processes
    - -case of H.M.: patient with temporal lobe removal
    - -anterograde amnesia: impairment of short-term memory consolidation

VERTEBRATE MODEL SYSTEMS
The Hippocampus
- Hippocampal trisynaptic circuit seems to model Hebb's cell assembly proposal
    - -dendritic spines of granule cells change their morphology upon synaptic activation through changes in their cytoskeletons
- Long-term Potentiation (LTP)
    - -following brief, high frequency stimulation of afferent fibers is a long lasting increase in synaptic strength
- Effects of Hippocampal Lesions
    - -spatial learning in rats is impaired when associations between external cues and location and space are necessary

Long-Term Potentiation (LTP)
- An increase in amplitude of the action potential and the EPSP that lasts for many hours after the stimulus events (See Figure 15-22)

-due to an increase in the efficiency of the synaptic transmission
- Appeal of LTP as a biological nemory system
    -concurrent activation of pre- and postsynaptic neurons
    -quickly initiated and long enduring changes in synaptic efficiency
- Mechanisms of LTP
    -convergence of simultaneous activity depolarizes the postsynaptic cell, activating the NMDA receptor, increasing Ca^{++} influx which stimulates protein kinase activity, triggering persistent postsynaptic changes
- LTP, Learning, and Memory
    -LTP has been demonstrated in hippocampal regions, as well as neocortical areas, brainstem and thalmic nuclei, and autonomic ganglia
    -LTP has been found in brain areas not associated with memory, suggesting that it may simply be a property of synapses

The Cerebellum and Nictitating Membrane Response

- The nictitating membrane response: A puff of air (US) to the eye elicits this reflexive response (UR)
    -initial studies revealed changes in hippocampal functioning though lesions of the hippocampal region did not impair learning
    -physiological changes in cerebellum recorded during associative learning

The Vestibulo-ocular Reflex

- Maintains an image's position on the retina when the head is moving.
    -Miles and Lisberger studied plasticity in VOR in monkeys

Lecture Topics:

1. During early fetal development, one of the great mysteries is how does one cell become many, and how do the many know where to go and what to do? This can serve as the basis of either class discussion or lecture. There is suggestion throughout the chapter that later forming cells receive information (e.g., cell proliferation, inside-out pattern of migration) from earlier forming cells. How might this information be shared and spread? What happens when the information is inaccurate?

2. One way to characterize learning is that it is a way of creating behavior. Given this, lecture could demonstrate how a given response may be "created" by using each of the forms of learning discussed in the chapter. What are the advantages of each type of learning? How complex may the behaviors be before the more simple types of learning are no longer effective as explanations?

3. A critical assumption made during studies of the biophysical and biochemical changes occurring during learning is that the process is the same or similar in simple and complex organisms. What are the exact premises and what is their likely truth? What evidence exist to support or refute the claim?

4. The research on LTP suggests (see pps. 386-7) that it may be a property of all synapses, not specifically designed, though well suited, to serve as the neurophysiological basis for memory. Lecture can be devoted to exploring this possibility and its implications, more fully. If LTP is common to all (or many) synapses, what does this suggest about the nature of memory? What does this suggest about the case of H.M., as well as the phenomena of amnesia and recovery from amnesia and repressed memories? Finally, if all neurons are capable of LTP, then what does this suggest about research relying upon lesions to provide evidence that a specific brain structure is responsible for learning or memory?

Overhead Transparencies:

1. Figure 15-2: Neural Tube Formation.

2. Figure 15-3: Human Brain Development.

3. Figure 15-4: Neural Tube Cell Proliferation.

4. Figure 15-11: Synapse Formation of the Neuromuscular Junction.

5. Figure 15-22: LTP in Hippocampal Pathways.

Classroom Demonstrations/Student Activities:

1. A number of software packages (typically those connected with Introduction to Psychology textbooks) allow students to condition an animated organism, typically a rat. Students do this by controlling the flow of food or some other reward. This software is a useful demonstration of the principles of operant conditioning.

2. Students may be asked to attempt to build (or at least describe) a model which displays characteristics of LTP. That is, build a system which changes as the result of experience. Such a system may be mechanical, a computer model, or simply conceptual.

Handouts:

The complex mechanisms displayed in the following figures could be prepared as handouts for student use:

1. Figure 15-16: Habituation of Gill-Withdrawal Reflex in *Aplysia*.

2. Figure 15-17: Sensitization of the Gill-Withdrawal Reflex in *Aplysia*.

3. Figure 15-18: Classical Conditioning in *Aplysia*.

4. Figure 15-22: LTP in Hippocampal Pathways.

5. Figure 15-23: Properties of LTP.

Video List:

1. The classic PBS video The Miracle of Life from 1980 provides stunning footage of early prenatal development which may provide useful background to the beginning of this chapter. There is some footage of nervous system development, including synaptogenesis.

2. The PBS series "The Mind" has several segments of interest. Episode two, Development has segments about prenatal and early

development in humans. Episode three, <u>Aging</u> has a number of segments about the impact of aging on the brain, especially memory functioning, and the impact of environmental stimulation on maintaining functioning later in life.

3. The PBS series "The Brain" has one episode (number 5), <u>Learning and Memory</u> which contains many segments related to the text. Segments include "The locus of learning and memory," "The hippocampus and memory," and "Learning as synaptic change."

CHAPTER 16: LANGUAGE AND HIGHER COGNITIVE FUNCTION

Chapter Outline:
HUMAN NEUROBIOLOGY
Theoretical limits and practical problems
- Search for the "command neuron" as an example
  - neurosurgery as an investigative tool
  - humans are uniquely capable of self-reflection
  - intrusive brain studies not possible, so we must study damaged brains that result from accidents only
  - although some control is possible, in human subjects control is limited: animals may be subjected to more stringent control

RESULTS FROM COMMUNICATION IN AND WITH OTHER SPECIES
- Activity in associative areas occurs immediately prior to activity in the adjacent motor cortex, prior to a behavior
- Animal communication
  - Washoe: monkey taught a system of symbols to communicate
  - Clever Hans: a circus horse who could apparently perform mathematical calculations

RESULTS FROM DIAGNOSTIC NEUROLOGY
- Diagnostic neurology: deduction of the location of central nervous system damage based on behavioral signs
  - magnetic resonance imaging (MRI) is a noninvasive means of exploring the structure of the brain
Aphasias
- Broca's aphasia: a speech production disorder with little impact on spoken or written comprehension: lethargic, labored speech, difficulty using grammar, difficulty with pronunciation, and anomia (difficulty in word use)
  - results from damage to Broca's area on the motor association cortex in the frontal lobe
- Wernicke's aphasia: difficulty in speech comprehension, but able to produce language normally; able to follow typical conventions of conversation, such as taking turns, reacting to facial expressions
  - results from damage to Wernicke's area on the left posterior region of the temporal lobe
  - there is a language circuit (See Figure 16-4) connecting Wernicke's and Broca's areas in the left hemisphere
Apraxias

- The "inability to make movement with cognitive intent"
  - -ideomotor apraxia: unable to perform simple motor tasks on command, though physically capable of performing the behavior
  - -constructional apraxia: cannot solve spatial problems or draw diagrams

Agnosias
- Posterior parietal zone
  - -if damaged causes a range of inabilities called angoras: inability to map world around the person
  - -decussation: it is possible to lack the ability to organize one half of the surroundings only, if only one hemisphere is damaged
  - -optic ataxia is the inability to locate and grasp objects
  - -persons able to see normally, but cannot grasp spatial relationships
  - -agnosia may be specific affecting only a single body part or location in the world

Alexias
- Alexia: writing without reading
  - -agraphia: reading without writing
  - -due to damage to left occipital lobe (association area adjacent to primary visual cortex) or disconnection syndromes, in which specific regions are intact but the connections between them are damaged

Dyslexias
- Impaired ability to read, competency below what would be expected given intelligence
  - -possibly due to a maturational lag, environmental deprivation, a defect of bilateralization between hemispheres, or abnormal connections between visual and language centers of the brain
  - -deep dyslexia: can understand most words, but cannot understand abstract words and verbs
  - -phonological dyslexia: reading is intact, but with pronounciation difficulties
  - -multiple forms make treatment difficult, but many dyslexics adapt

The concept of Latent Circuits and Latent Function
- Although cell development in CNS stops before adulthood and new connection do not form after myelination is complete in adolescence, the brain is able to recover from damage throughout life

-latent function: function which is normally suppressed, either by inhibitory neurons or hemispheric dominance, which is expressed when these areas are damaged
-most synapses are supernumerary, then are eliminated during maturation not as a loss of function but rather a refinement

Emotion

- Physiological constituents: CNS, ANS, neurohormonal and visceral activity
    -behavioral indicators: facial expressions, tone of voice, posture, vocal activity
    -cognitive indicators: self-inferred state, including memories and ideas
- Emotion is a multiple structure system
    -initial sensory information is received and processed through the cortex to association cortex then higher level processing, such as combining with other sensory or memory information
    -limbic system: may be responsible for emotion expression
    -frontal cortex, inferior temporal cortex, paralimbic cortex, and the amygdala
- Effects of frontal lobe lesions
    -primates: reduced social interactions, poor social conduct and altered social behavior, and diminished vocalizations, facial expression, and body gestures
    -humans: right hemisphere lesions result in speech lacking prosody, and poor performance on tests of humor and social nuance, but were more socially garrulous; left hemisphere lesions result in decreased talking
    -stimulating thalamus and hypothalamus results in specific emotional responses

Memory

- No single part of the brain seems to hold a memory
- Hippocampal formation
    -source of memory for places and spatial relations, area necessary for working memory, and damage to hippocampus and amygdala produce deficits in recognition memory
- Amygdala also implicated for emotional memories
    -implicit memory: unconscious and unintentional
    -explicit memory: conscious
    -infantile amnesia: early memories are present but unable to be retrieved
    -posttraumatic amnesia: memory loss resulting from accidents

-global transient amnesia: significant anterograde and retrograde amnesia

ORGANIC BRAIN SYNDROMES

Down Syndrome
- Called trisomy 21 (3 copies of chromosome 21)
    -leads to development of abnormally small brain, abnormalities in shape and size of temporal lobes, and developmental disability

Phenylketonuria
- Genetic abnormality due to a recessive, autosomal gene that cannot program enough enzymatic activity to metabolize phenylalanine
    -can lead to microcephaly, or small head, and mental retardation

Cerebellar Ataxia (also called pugilistic dementia)
- Results from repeated jarring blows to the head
    -"Punch drunk"-similar syndrome resulting from a single blow

Korsakoff's Disease
- A disease resulting from extended periods alcohol as the sole dietary intake
    -due to a lack of thiamine in the diet due to reliance upon alcohol as diet

Spongiform Encephalopathies
- Creutzfeldt-Jakob disease
    -affects older adults, causing dementia, shock-like contractions, violent twitches, speech disturbances, inability to coordinate movement
    -role of viruses
    -scrapie, a spongiform in sheep, mediated by a virus made of proteins (prions)
    -Multiple Sclerosis, an autoimmune disease when myelin sheath degenerates, and lateral sclerosis (Lou Gherig's Disease) may also be caused by prions
    -Kuru: spongiform certain to be mediated by prions
    -transmitted by New Guinea tribespeople who ritualistically consume brains of relatives who have died (including the prion)

Alzheimer's Disease
- A progressive disease occurring in mid- to late life which is irreversible and incurable characterized by loss of memory
    -two cytological signs:

-plaques (lesions) containing abnormally high amounts of protein ß-amyloid

-neurofibrillary tangles, masses of disorganized nerve fiber ß-amyloid accumulation may be due to disordered processing of the precursor protein, leaving it to accumulate in the plaques

-neurofibrillary tangles may be induced by aluminum cation

EPILEPSY

- Because the brain is predominated by inhibitory channels over excitatory, when the inhibitory channels break down, unbounded excitation may appear

   -epilepsy may be caused by abnormal potassium channel functioning

   -epileptic seizures: behavioral result of a release of inhibitory channels

   -tonic phase: stiffening of the body

   -clonic phase: following body stiffness is a period of shaking caused by simultaneous bursting of excitatory cells within the cortex

   -if the focus is in association cortex patients often report an aura or premonition

   -larger spread produces petit mal seizures involving parts of the body, or grand mal seizures involving the whole body (and are life threatening)

   -most epileptics treated with drugs enhancing GABA-mediated inhibition of the brain, previous treatment included severing of the corpus collosum

RESULTS FROM NONINVASIVE IMAGING TECHNIQUES

Position Emission Tomography (PET)

- Uses a positron emitting nuclide which enters the brain through the blood

   -when positron collides with an electron two gamma rays are emitted

Magnetic Resonance Imaging (MRI)

- Detects resonance found in the bonds between two chemicals

Computerized Axial Tomography (CAT)

- Based upon x-ray technology in which a central X-ray tube and detector are used to take a sequence of 12 images which are then combined to provide an image

Cerebral Blood Flow Measurements

120

- Compares the chemical content of arterial and venous blood flow

Electrical and Magnetic Records across the Skull
- Magnetic equivalent of EEG measured by a magnetoencephalogram (MEG)

RESULTS FROM BRAIN STIMULATION

Neurosurgery on Awake Individuals
- A person's reports during surgery guide the surgeon to find the exact location and nature of the damage sustained

Penfield's Observations
- Penfield would stimulate areas of the brain and ask patients to report any feelings or thoughts
    -interpretation of these findings
    -cellular connectionism: brain regions have specialized functions
    -aggregate field theory: function is a property of a network of cells

CONSCIOUSSNESS AND THE SELF

Is it Possible to be "Less of a Person"?
- Inability to understand the passage of time
    -sense of "self"

Lecture Topics:

1. There are several instances where sex differences are described in the chapter. The source of these differences is a question which leads to interesting discussion. On the one hand these differences could reflect genetic differences between men and women. On the other hand, they may reflect developmental differences in the brain due to different experiences of males and females in society. Students may explore these and other possibilities in discussion or in debate form.

2. How to study human neurobiology is a difficult issue, though it has become increasingly accepted. Lecture can focus on historical trends in how brain function is investigated, starting with reliance on post-mortem exams to modern brain surgery and non-invasive techniques. It may be possible that one or more students have had one or more of these procedures done, or sample slides may be obtained from local hospitals to use as visual aides.

3. Neurological abnormalities, be they inherited at conception or the result of behaviors during life (e.g., drinking) often result in profound changes in the person, especially in personality and memory. This makes our sense of self fragile, susceptible to upheaval with any number of occurrences. The chapter ends with a discussion of consciousness, the most "human" attribute we have. How are consciousness and self related? What is their nature? Are they permanent? If so, how do they develop, yet stay the same? Is a person who suffers a stroke, or similar brain damage, a different person?

4. Examining the causes (that are known) of the various dysfunctions presented in the text reveals a broad range, including pure genetic defects (Trisomy 21, Phenylketonuria) to purely environmental events (Cerebellar ataxia, spongiform encephalopathies) to disorders involving both (Alzheimer's). The nature-nurture debate serves as the basis of compelling discussions about the nature of these defects.

Overhead Transparencies:

1. Figure16-4: The Speech Circuit.

2. Figure16-5: Topographical Map of the Cerebral Cortex.

3. Figure16-8: Limbic Structures and Memory.

4. Figure16-10: Brain Structures Contributing to Memory.

5. Figure 16-20: Brain Function and Regional Blood Flow.

Classroom Demonstrations/Student Activities:

1. To demonstrate the challenges of communication with other species, have students work pairs with one student the "teacher" and the other the non-language "learner." Have the teacher develop a set of simple signs then try to teach the learner to identify objects and perform certain actions, but without being able to use verbal language.

2. A range of software is available on the market (e.g., MEL, MindLab) that allow for instructors to develop simple reaction time studies. Using this software, tasks may be designed involving the use of mental imagery, language skills, or spatial reasoning. Students perform these tasks and record their reaction time data. This data may then be used as the basis of describing the underlying brain activity (or time) required to complete different tasks. Also illustrated are individual differences which exist in processing speed and efficiency.

Handouts:

1. A handout of Table 16-1 is a valuable resource for students.

2. A list of noninvasive imaging techniques and how they work is a good resource.

Video List:

1. Epilepsy: Breaking the barrier, available through Films for the Humanities and Sciences is a brief (20 minute) program about the identification and treatment of epilepsy. This video includes beautiful imagery of various noninvasive imaging techniques.

2. Special needs students in regular classrooms? Sean's story, available through Films for the Humanities and Sciences follows a year in the life of an 8-year-old with Down's Syndrome. This video

addresses issue in mainstreaming, and is not highly biological, but is a nice introduction to capabilities and circumstances of Down's kids.

3. <u>Dyslexia: A different kind of mind</u> produced by Dartmouth-Hitchcock Medical Center is a brief overview of dyslexia and educational programs designed as interventions. This video highlights the uniqueness of the talents of dyslexics and so has a very positive feel to it. It is not biological in nature.

4. Several episodes from the PBS series "The Mind" are relevant to the material in this chapter. Episode #1 has a brief segment on language and brain differences between ape and human. It also has a segment about Clive Wearing, a man with memory loss. Episode #7, <u>Language</u> includes excellent summaries of research in the area (though a bit out-dated). Segment #8, <u>Thinking</u> is also a nice summary of somewhat dated research, though it does have a nice description of brain imaging techniques.

5. Several episodes of the PBS series "The Brain" are relevant. Episode #5, <u>Learning and Memory</u> has several pertinent segments. There are clips about short-term memory, the location of memory and the hippocampus. Episode #6, <u>The Two Brains</u> has a brief segment on Broca and Wernicke as well as a segment on the "split brain." Episode #7 <u>States of Mind</u>, has a brief piece on Alzheimer's.

CHAPTER 17: PSYCHOPHARMACOLOGY

Chapter Outline:
AGONISTS AND ANTAGONISTS
- Drugs influence brain by influencing synaptic transmission or by mimicking an endogenous transmitter
    -agonist: a drug which mimics the actions of an endogenous transmitter
    -antagonist: a drug which prevents normal activity of a transmitter

PHARMACOKINETICS
Administration
- The first step in drug uptake; how the drug enters the body
Distribution
- Drug distribution depends primarily upon the ability for drugs to diffuse across cell membranes however, most drug action effects synaptic activity outside cells
    -to produce effects, drugs must act on specific receptors or synapses
Elimination
- Half-life: the amount of time it takes to eliminate 50% of the drug from the body
    -drug metabolism typically by the liver, broken down to (metabolites)

ADDICTION, TOLERANCE AND WITHDRAWAL
- Tolerance: more and more of the drug is required to produce a desired effect
- Addiction: physiological and psychological need for a drug
    -withdrawal: often painful physical and psychological symptoms opposite from those the drug induces
    -Opponent process theory: the body strives towards homeostasis
    -a drug produces perturbations from homeostasis (A-process)
    -body tries to reduce perturbations by producing opposite effects (B-process)
    -tolerance: increasing strength of the B-process with increases in the A-process
    -addiction: need for more A-process to counteract the negative B-process

-withdrawal: the removal of the A-process, leaving behind a strengthened, opposite, B-process

CENTRAL NERVOUS SYSTEM DEPRESSANTS
Alcohol and Marijuana

- Alcohol
    - -administration: consumed in beverage form
    - -distribution: alcohol passes through the stomach (poor absorption) and enters small intestine (rapid absorption)
    - -alcohol is a depressant: effects include visual impairment, lack of motor coordination, increased reaction time, euphoria, and release from inhibitions
    - -elimination: alcohol is metabolized by the liver
    - -long-term effects of alcohol
    - -Korsakoff's diseases: debilitating memory loss
    - -cirrhosis is a weakening of the liver due to excessive metabolism of alcohol
    - -fetal alcohol syndrome appears in children of mothers who drink during pregnancy; symptoms include low birth weight, and low IQ
- Marijuana
    - -low/moderate doses: sedative-hypnotic; high doses: euphoria & hallucination
    - -administration: typically inhaled via pipe or cigarette, though may be eaten
    - -distribution: absorption is via inhaling, entering blood stream through lungs
    - -elimination: half-life after distributed to fat is 30 hours (as high as 4 days)
    - -short-term effects: subtle mood alterations and euphoria, increased appetite and distortion of perception of time
    - -marijuana has been used for reduction of pain among glaucoma patients, and alleviation of nausea for chemotherapy and AIDS patients
    - -long-term effects: less severe than chronic alcohol use
    - -major health threats are lung pathologies, some data suggest immunosuppression

Mechanisms of Action: Membrane Theories

- Alcohol: causes the neuronal membrane to become more flexible, reducing efficiency of neuronal transmission, and disrupt activity of membrane receptors
- Marijuana: THC recently affects a specific receptor site

Mechanisms of Action: Receptor Theories
- Alcohol
    -does influence activity of the GABA receptor and the methyl-d-asparate (NMDA) receptor (a subtype of glutamate receptor)
    -alcohol produces inhibition by enhancing the action of GABA and reducing the activity of an excitatory neuroreceptor
- Marijuana
    -recent research isolated a specific cannabinoid receptor in rat brains
    -receptors in areas responsible for euphoria, relaxation, and temporal distortions

Sedatives and Tranquilizers
- Barbiturates: class of synthetic compounds (not found in nature)
    -usually taken orally and distributed to the body through the blood stream
    -differ in their length of action (e.g., phenobarbital has a half life of 80-100 hrs)
    -In low doses effects include euphoria and loss of inhibition
- Benzodiazepines: synthetic compounds used extensively as antianxiety drugs
    -common forms include chlordiazepoxide (Librium) and diazepam (Valium)
    -usually taken orally and distributed to the body through the blood stream
    -facilitate GABA activity; have binding sites on GABA receptors

Mechanism of Action: The Prospect of Natural Ligands
- Search for natural ligands
    -inverse agonists: substances that do not block transmitter activity, but bind to receptor sites and produce effects opposite those of an agonist

Mechanisms of Action: Chloride Conductance and CNS Output
- CNS depressants act on GABA, an inhibitory transmitter
    -GABA opens chloride channels (Cl^-), producing hyperpolarization

CENTRAL NERVOUS SYSTEM STIMULANTS
Nicotine and Caffeine
- Nicotine
    -administration: most commonly ingested through inhaling, though comparable blood levels are reached by chewing

-distribution: absorption through lungs is almost as efficient as through IV
-elimination
-nicotine is metabolized into inactive compounds with a half life of 2 hours
-effects of nicotine: a CNS stimulant, produces feelings of alertness also increases irritability, suppresses hunger (leading to weight loss), increased blood pressure and heart rate
-health risks: "the leading cause of preventable, premature death in the world"
-although effects are mediated by nicotine, all long-term toxicities are due to tars and other chemicals resulting from burning cigarettes
-most associated disease is cancers (primarily lung) and heart disease

- Caffeine
-administration: 80% of adults drink 3 cups of coffee per day
-distribution: absorbed rapidly through lumen in the gut
-significant blood levels within 30 minutes, effects peak after 2 hours
-elimination: half life of 3-5 hours
-effects: caffeine is an adenosine receptor, which plays a role in sedation and bronchospasm-blockage; produces mental alertness and bronchodilation. Increase in alertness and decrease in fatigue, relaxes the bronchi. May also create nervousness and encourage hypertension. In high doses may cause irritability, insomnia, and nervousness.

Amphetamines and Cocaine

- Amphetamines
-administration: oral or nasal ingestion, also IV ingestion is common
-distribution: circulates via blood stream
-elimination: metabolized by liver with a half life of 18-24 hours
-effects: increase in blood pressure, motor activity, libido, and pain threshold, ecreases in bronchial muscle tone, fatigue, and appetite, euphoria. High doses result in paranoia. Overdose causes cerebral hemorrhage
- Cocaine
-administration: ingested nasally, in the form of crack can be smoked

-distribution: when ingested nasally it is absorbed by the mucosal membranes, when inhaled it is absorbed directly into the blood through the lungs

-elimination: Metabolized by a specific esterase then eliminated from the body with a half life of 15-30 minutes

-effects: increased heart rate, blood pressure, and body temperature; feelings of euphoria; In high doses acts as a local anesthesia by blocking Na^+ channels

-long term health risks: cardiovascular or cerebrovascular problems

Mechanisms of Action: Dopamine Autoreceptors

* Receptors on both the presynaptic and postsynaptic membranes

    -postsynaptic receptors may be inhibitory or excitatory, alpha or beta subtypes

    -autoreceptors are homeostatic, shutting down a transmission once it occurs

    -autoreceptors difficult to distinguish from autapses (self association synapses)

Mechanisms of Action: Dopamine Re-uptake

* Catecholamines are inactivated by re-uptake at the synapse achieved by a protein that binds to transmitter and transports it back to the presynaptic cell

    -cocaine and amphetamines prevent this process amplifying the effects

    -amphetamines increase release of transmitters, extending its activity time

HALLUCINOGENS

* Peyote (active ingredient is mescaline)

    -taken orally in the form of buttons (dried cactus tops)

    -absorbed rapidly by the gut, significant levels in the brain at 30-60 minutes

    -effects: in small doses effects increase in blood pressure, heart rate, and pupil dilation. In higher doses hallucinations (visions of animals or people)

* Ecstasy (MDMA: 3,4-methylenedioxymethamphetamine): synthetic of mescaline

* LSD (lysergic acid diethylamide)

    -taken orally as blots on paper or sugar cubes

    -onset of 30-60 minutes, half life is 3 hours, effects last 10-12 hrs

-effects: increase heart rate and blood pressure, pupil dilation, perceptual alterations, occasionally psychotic episodes and synesthesia, or mixing of senses

-tolerance does develop, but addiction apparently do not.

-greatest risk is a psychotic break possibly leading to suicide

- Psilocybin ("Magic mushrooms")

    -after oral ingestion, body converts it to psilocin (200x less powerful than LSD)

    -produces distortions of thought and perception

- PCP (Phenylcyclohexyl piperadine; "angel dust")

    -ingested orally; effects last from 4-6 hrs

    -produces a trance-like state (dissociative anesthetic), but not hallucinations

Mechanisms of Action: Results of Neuropharmacology

- Aghajanian and Haigler (1974) studied cellular action of LSD

    -LSD acts as a serotonin agonist at inhibitory autoreceptors

    -many hallucinogens are structurally similar to endogenous transmitters

OPIATES

- Morphine: most potent derivative of opium

    -administered through various routes, typically IV

    -circulates through blood then eliminated by liver

    -effects include analgesia, euphoria, sedation, respiratory depression, cough suppression, pupilary constriction, also nausea and asthma-like symptoms

- Heroin: synthetic derivative of morphine

    -approximately 10 times more powerful

Mechanisms of Action: Heterogeneity of Opiate Receptors

- Types of Opiate receptors

    -mu opiate receptor: important for production of analgesia

    -kappa: analgesic effects by blocking pain signal at spinal cord

    -delta: involved in altering affect and euphoria

    -sigma: involved in dysphoria, feelings of discomfort

Mechanisms of Action: Natural Opiate Agonists and Synthetic Opiate Antagonists

- Endogenous opiates: enkephalins, ß-endorphin, and dynorphins

    -pharmaceutical antagonists: naloxene and naltrexone

Lecture Topics:

1. Many of the substances described in this chapter have severe effects taken in heavy doses, but less severe, perhaps pleasant effects in lower doses. Some of these substances are illegal while others are not. A discussion about why some drugs are legal despite their greater negative effects than some drugs which are illegal should focus of biological, psychological, sociological, and legal aspects of this debate.

2. As part of #1 above, or as a separate topic, students may use tobacco and smoking as a case study of regulation of drugs. Issues include attempts to regulate teen smoking, additives to tobacco, tobacco company liability in class-action and individual civil suits, and prohibitions against smoking in public.

3. For many of the drugs discussed in the chapter, the mode of action is not well known. A lecture may be devoted to describing the process of investigation that course when identifying modes of action (perhaps a psychopharmacologist presentation). Students should b encouraged to formulate their own hypotheses and test them against existing knowledge.

4. Evolution theory has provided compelling arguments about the development of many characteristics. A lecture may be devoted to exploring how the substances described in this chapter may have evolved, either in humans (endogenous systems), or nature. Care should be given to the distinction between early humans and our current state, especially regarding recreational use of drugs (now) versus their ingestion while searching for food (survival).

Overhead Transparencies:

1. Figure 17-1: The Blood-Brain Barrier.

2. Figure 17-11: Autoreceptors and Autapses.

3. Figure from Box 17-2: The Problem of Specificity.

4. Figure 17-14: LSD Action on the Raphe Nucleus.

Classroom Demonstrations/Student Activities:

1. Are the effects of drugs all in the head? Students may be

persuaded to behave in ways consistent with drug use if they believe they have ingested the drug, suggesting that biochemical action is not the only mode of action of drugs. Randomly assign students to two groups: subjects and observers. Be sure that all subjects are of legal drinking age (make this an overt part of the assignment to groups). Pass out to all subjects three cups filled with lightly flavored water. Tell them this is a highly expensive and potent form of alcohol. Ask the subjects to perform a series of motor tasks, such as arranging a sequence of pictures, assembling a puzzle, copying line drawings. Have the observers evaluate the subjects' performance. Also have the "subjects" record their thoughts during the procedure. Depending upon the level of belief (and the acting of the instructor), many of the "observers" will report drunken behavior and decreased capacity of the subjects, and subjects' performance may well suffer, and their reports will be consistent with having consumed alcohol.

2.   Students who smoke, or drink alcohol, or use some other drug discussed in the chapter, may attempt to quit, at least for a period of time, to demonstrate the powerful addiction and withdrawal effects. Some students may experiment with methods of quitting (e.g., hypnosis, the patch for smokers, weaning) and chart changes which occur to their mood and physiology. They may rate their activity level, mood, chart blood pressure and heart rate, as well as rate overall level of "withdrawal discomfort" during the time period of quitting.

Handouts:

1.   Handouts containing the chemical make-up of drugs discussed in the chapter is a useful reference for students.

2.   A table listing each drug discussed in the chapter and their presumed mechanisms of action (as presented in the chapter).

Video List:

1.   Bill Moyer's recent series on "Addiction" provides numerous examples of the effects of drugs on persons. Included are segments are the neurobiology of drugs and addiction. Made in the middle 1990's the series offers contemporary research summaries and legal and societal positions on substance use and abuse. Use all or part of this series.

2. Unborn addicts, a video available through Films for the Humanities and Sciences, follows the course of two pregnant addicts, ending in birth and treatment. There is a strong scene of infant withdrawal, so be advised.

3. The theatrical release Leaving Las Vegas is about a man trying to kill himself by drinking alcohol. This very powerful film offers a stark depiction of Korsakoff's disease. Note that this film has graphic depictions of sex, including prostitution and rape (MPA Rating of R).

4. The PBS series "The Mind" has two epsiodes which are relevant here. The first (Episode #2: Development) contains a brief discussion of fetal alcohol syndrome. The second is an entire epsiode (#4: Addictions) about addiction, primarily to depressants and particularly alcohol. Both of these are redundant with numbers 1 and 3 listed above, but provide briefer, though slightly older, video material.

CHAPTER 18: THE BIOLOGY OF MENTAL ILLNESS

Chapter Outline:

THE TAXONOMY OF MENTAL ILLNESS: THE DSM IV

* Early pioneers in psychiatry
  -Kraepelin and "premature senility"
  -Bleuler and schizophrenia
  -the biological basis for mental illness is the goal of psychiatry
  The diagnostic and statistical manual
  -contrast between disorders which are biological in nature and those that are psychological in nature
  -how many cases of mental illness fall into each of these two categories?
  -the mind/body problem revisited
  -monism v. dualism

SCHIZOPHRENIA

About Schizophrenia

* Group of disorders, including 6-month period of disturbances of communication, perception, or thought processes
* Key distinctions
  -not a mood disorder
  -almost certainly due to biological causes
  -not multiple personality syndrome
  -disorder of the apprehension of reality
* Models of schizophrenia
  -inability to segregate relevant and irrelevant sensory stimulation and/or memories
  -sensory abnormality producing "false" realities
  -hallucinations
  -synesthesia: sensory input attributed to different modality (e.g., hearing colors)
* Symptoms
  -florid symptoms: presence of distinctive behaviors, including disorganized thinking, paranoia, delusions of grandeur, and bizarre ideation
  -negative symptoms (absence of normal and social behavior: neglect of personal hygiene, odd behavior and ideas, social isolation, withdrawal, and catatonia) often precede florid symptoms
* Challenges to effective treatment

-spontaneous remission
-spontaneous relapse
-"rule of thirds": after onset, 1/3 spontaneously recover, 1/3 spontaneous remission and relapse, controlled by medication, 1/3 chronically ill

Neuroleptic Drugs

- Trend in hospitalization
  -upward climb during early 1900s probably due to better diagnosis
  -decline marked by the introduction of first drug therapy for schizophrenia called chlorpromazine (thorazine)
- About neuroleptic drugs
  -since chlorpromazine many have been synthesized and used
  -when effective quickly reduce the florid symptoms of schizophrenia
  -has a sedative effect on non-schizophrenics

Parallel with Dopamine Binding

- The dopaminergic hypothesis
  -neuroleptic drugs bind to dopamine receptors as antagonists
  -atypical neuroleptics bind to both dopamine and serotonin
  -clinical efficacy is a function of how well the drugs bind with dopamine
  -this suggests that the underlying deficiency in schizophrenia is too much dopamine transmission in parts of the brain.
- Evaluating the hypothesis
  -post-mortem data (Figure 18-7) showing higher of dopamine than norepinephrine in schizophrenic patients than normals
  -does not explain how the dopamine levels became so high

So Many Choices

- The number of possible drugs is a function of the number of possible control mechanisms (receptor sites and types), and different regions of the brain which may be affected
  -there are many systems in the nervous system that utilize dopamine:
  -sympathetic ganglia, small intensity fluorescent cells (autonomic function)
  -nigrostriatal projection (extrapyramidal motor behavior)
  -tuberoinfundibular projection (release of pituitary peptides)
  -mesocortical system (gateway for interpretation of stimuli)
- Effects of neuroleptics at specific brain sites

-the side effects of neuroleptics are opposite to the effects of dopamine, thus, they do not create pleasurable or reward feelings.

-because neuroleptic drugs resemble dopamine agonists structurally, they bind to at all dopiminergic sites, creating a range of effects

- Affinity and Ligands

-drugs will have varying affinity for receptor sites

-specific ligands and selective ligands

-pharmaceutical companies have found only selective ligands

Receptor theories

- Receptor number and affinity may be influenced developmentally (Fig. 18-8)

-down-regulation and up-regulation

Difficulty in diagnosis

- Heterogeneity of symptoms (Table 18-1)

-Type I: florid symptoms

-Type II: negative symptoms

-commonalty of symptoms with other illnesses

Genetic Factors and Structural Differences

- Studies of genetically identical individuals reared together and apart found a modest but significant correlation between shared genes and development of schizophrenia

-PET scans suggested that schizophrenics had larger cerebral ventricles than age-matched controls

A Viral Cause?

- Medical records from Denmark revealed a dramatic increase in the birthrate of schizophrenics among women who developed influenza during the second trimester of pregnancy (Figure 18-10)

AFFECTIVE DISORDERS

Distinctions Between Affective Disorders and Others

- Person perceives reality normally, but feelings about that reality may be distorted in some way

Mania

- Symptoms include accelerated thought process, euphoria, exaggerated sexual or physical appetite, illusions of invincibility, and grandiose ambitions

-effectively treated by lithium and other drugs

Unipolar and Bipolar Illness

- Mania often relapses, but often leads into a period of depression

Symptoms of depression: suicidal thoughts. anhedonia (lack of pleasure in food, sex, or exercise), psychomotor retardation, expressions of helplessness, hopelessness, and worthlessness, sleep disturbances resulting in lost REM sleep

- Unipolar illness
    -periods of depression alternate with normal periods
- Bipolar illness
    -brief periods of mania oscillate with brief periods of depression and prolonged periods of normalcy

A Diagnostic Continuum

- Most people experience some periods of sadness
    -drug therapy helps people all along the continuum of depression

A Disorder of Circadian Rhythmicity?

- Seasonal affective disorder (SAD)
    -most commonly occurs in the winter in Northern climates
    -symptoms include morning hypersomnia, weight gain, increased appetite, low energy
    -treatment: use of strong artificial light to mimic the sun

The Design and Pursuit of Antidepressant Drugs

- The Monoamine Hypothesis
    -monoamine antagonists can produce depression
    -the problem remains which monoamine, which location, and which mode of action?
- Monoamine oxidase (MAO)
    -it was believed that depression is caused by too little catecholamine in the brain, so MAO inhibitors were used to allow more catecholamine to remain in the brain
    -these drugs were pargyline, and later clorgyline and selegine (Deprenyl)
    -amphetamines have the same effect
    -because these drugs affect all catecholamine action in the body there are a number of side effects
- Tricyclic Antidepressants
    -developed as an effort to find a drug which affects only those receptor sites central to depression
- Atypical Antidepressants
    -selective serotonin re-uptake inhibitors: raise extracellular levels of serotonin (e.g., Prozac (fluoxetine), Zoloft (sertraline), and Paxil (paroxetine))

ANXIETY DISORDERS

- Symptoms: intense dread and generalized avoidance behavior not attributable to any real cause
    -treatment through anxiolytics (from the benzodiazepine family) which act as tranquilizers

THE HAZARDS OF MEDICATION
- Potential drawbacks to using psychotropic drugs include:
    -poorly understood modes of action may hide unknown side-effects
    -prescriptive drugs may be addictive and create withdrawal effects
    -medication may exacerbate preexisting conditions
    -drugs taken in combination may be lethal
    -long-term maintenance produces trophic consequences which are poorly understood

Lecture Topics:

1. In several sections of the chapter, the text indicates the difficulty of providing clear lines of demarcation between "well" and "ill." This idea of a continuum is a powerful basis for discussion. Students may consider how to draw the line. Use contemporary examples, such as Dennis Rodman (basketball) or Ronald Reagan (former President) to show how behaviors are typically used to make the judgment.

2. The effects of drug therapy are not only immediate, occurring concurrently with medication, but some also persist after cessation of treatment. This suggests that in some cases there is a structural change which occur through treatment that may not be able to be undone. Given this, what are the ethical and moral issues confronting doctors, researchers, and pharmacologists in pursuing drug therapy.

3. Based upon the discussion of drug therapy in this chapter, and the discussion of consciousness (Chapter 16), students may reconsider the mind-body problem, this time in the context of biological manipulation of the body and the consequences for the mind.

4. A number of authors and film-makers have produced works depicting a futuristic society addicted to drugs, totally dependent upon drugs to experience all "natural" emotions. With the popularity of Prozac and other mood enhancing, legal drugs, are we headed to

that future? Does it matter that the drugs are legal, illegal, or naturally occurring (e.g. St. John's wort)?

Overhead Transparencies:

1. Figure 18-3: Model of Cognitive Abnormalities and Symptoms of Schizophrenia.

2. Figure 18-5: The Greatest Success Story of Biological Psychiatry.

3. Figure 18-7: Comparison of Dopamine/Norepinephrine in Normal and Schizophrenic Subjects.

4. Figure 18-9: Data Supporting the Theory that Schizophrenics Have Larger Cerebral Ventricles.

5. The "potential drawbacks to the use of psychotropic drugs" on page 452.

Classroom Demonstrations/Student Activities:

1. To demonstrate "normal" fluctuations in mood, students can keep an "affect log," tracking their mood over a period of several days or a week. Tell students to rate their mood from -3 (really sad) to +3 (really happy) every four hours that they are awake, as well as when they wake-up and go to bed. Students could hand in graphs (without names) of their ratings and they could be compiled and compared.

2. There are a number of legal issues concerning the rights of individuals to receive and refuse treatment for medical conditions. Students may research this legal issue then be divided into two teams to debate when a person has the right to refuse medication and when he/she does not have that right. These same issues may considered as they regard children or persons of limited intellectual capacity, cases where others may seek to exercise these rights for the individual.

Handouts:

1. Copy of the DSM diagnostic criteria for schizophrenia, depression, mania, and anxiety disorders may be provided.

2. A handout listing common forms of mental illness and their drug therapies may be useful.

Video List:

1. Jonathan Miller's series "Madness", episode 3, Brainwaves, provides a history of the treatment of mental illness, including footage of electroconvulsive therapy and other early attempts to control mental illness. The video also presents the case of Nazi experimentation on humans and asks "How different is our contemporary approach?" This is a stark and moving series.

2. In The Madness of King George, attempts are made to restore the King's sanity. This theatrical release provides a marvelous examination of definitions of mental illness as well as modes of treatment.

3. Awakenings, both the film and the book by Oliver Sacks, is a dramatic story about the use of drug therapy on mentally ill persons. The film version is particularly good at depicting how psychiatrists explore modes of treatment, and the effects treatment has on patients and patient families.

4. The PBS series "The Mind" has an entire episode (#6: Depression) concerning the etiology, treatment, and biology of affective disorders. Though a bit older, much of the content is applicable to current understanding, or lends itself to a brief addendum presentation by the instructor.

5. The PBS series "The Brain" has two relevant episodes. Episode #7 ("Madness") depicts etiology, treatment, and biology of schizophrenia. Epsiode #8 ("States of Mind") has a brief section about multiple presonality disorders. This is an older series, but much of the content is still accurate or amenable to brief corrections or expansions through lecture.